Books by Richard Bissell

A STRETCH ON THE RIVER
THE MONONGAHELA
7½ CENTS
HIGH WATER
SAY, DARLING
GOODBYE, AVA
YOU CAN ALWAYS TELL A HARVARD MAN
STILL CIRCLING MOOSE JAW
HOW MANY MILES TO GALENA?
JULIA HARRINGTON

Drama
THE PAJAMA GAME
(with George Abbott)

SAY, DARLING
(with Abe Burrows and Marian Bissell)

JULIA HARRINGTON
Winnebago, Iowa
1913

JULIA HARRINGTON
Winnebago, Iowa
1913

Text and Illustrations by

Richard Bissell

Little, Brown and Company • Boston • Toronto

LIBRARY OF CONGRESS CATALOG CARD NO. 70-86617

Second Printing

Published simultaneously in Canada
by Little, Brown & Company (Canada) Limited

PRINTED IN THE UNITED STATES OF AMERICA

'JULIA

HARRINGTON

Yes, an "IVAN HOE"
BEYOND A QUESTION
IS THE FARMERS IDEAL
OF PERFECTION
SIMPLY SUPERB

MADE ONLY BY
WITHINGTON & COOLEY MFG CO.
JACKSON, MICH., U.S.A.

WINNEBAGO

IOWA

1913

PURE
GRANULATED SOAP.
ECONOMICAL, CONVENIENT,
AND POPULAR.
MADE BY
D. W. WILLIAMS & CO.

I

My name is Julia Harrington. I am twelve years old going on thirteen. I attend the Prescott School where I am in the Eighth Grade. My teacher is Miss Prohaska, the most popular teacher in the school.

My Papa owns the EMPORIUM, a dry goods and fancy goods store on Main Street across from the Railroad Station. Salesmen come from Omaha and Kansas City and St. Louis and Dubuque and Chicago to sell goods to Papa. They "show their lines," as they call it, in the "sample room" at the Hawkeye Hotel.

Our town is Winnebago, Iowa, an Indian name and a pretty one. It was founded by James Perley Lord in the year 1841. Population 8,651 and located on the North Branch of the Upper Antelope River. We are served by the Chicago and Northwestern Railroad on the double-track Main Line between Chicago and points west. However, the crack express trains naturally do not stop here. The railroad is always called "The Northwestern."

The men who work for the railroad have a joke Papa told me:

They say, "There are two ways to do things: the easy way and the Northwestern way."

I don't understand it, really.

My best friend is Harriet Hackenbush who lives up Osage Street one block, and one block to the left on Prairie Ave. Her Papa owns the "Oriental Sweet Shoppe" next to the Paris Theatre. How would you like to have a best friend whose Papa owned a Sweet Shoppe?

There are many stylish homes in Winnebago, both quaint and stately, of which we are justly proud. Can you guess which one is the humble abode of

Julia Harrington
22 Osage Street
Winnebago
Adams County
Iowa
United States of America
North America
Western Hemisphere
The World
The Universe
September 1913

$7.39 PAINTS THIS HOUSE, 23X34-20 FEET HIGH, TWO COATS.

Colors and quantity of each required:

BODY { 3 gallons No. 30Y0252 Oakwood for lower half { 3 gals. at 98c per gal... $2.94
{ 3 gallons No. 30Y0226 Willow Green for upper half { 3 gals. at 98c per gal... 2.94
TRIMMING, 1½ gallons No. 30Y0243 White for........................... 1.51

Total.......$7.39

Roof will require 4 gals. No 30Y800 Red Roof Paint at 65c per gallon, $2.60 additional.

$10.08 PAINTS THIS HOUSE, 26X46-20 FEET HIGH, TWO COATS.

Colors and quantity of each required:

BODY, 9 gallons No. 30Y0240 Yellow Stone { 5 gallons at 93c per gallon....$4.65
{ 4 gallons at 98c per gallon.... 3.92
TRIMMING, 1½ gallons No. 30Y0235 Light Stone for...................... 1.51

Total.........$10.08

Roof will require 5 gals. No. 30Y860 Green Roof Paint at 60c per gal., $3.00 additional.

$9.55 PAINTS THIS HOUSE, 22X40-20 FEET HIGH, TWO COATS.

Colors and quantity of each required:

BODY, 8 gallons No. 30Y0226 Willow Green { 5 gallons at 93c per gallon $4.65
{ 3 gallons at 98c per gallon 2.94
TRIMMING, 2 gallons No. 30Y0208 Pearl, at 98c per gallon 1.96

Total.........$9.55

Roof will require 5 gals. No. 30Y800 Red Roof Paint at 60 cents per gal., $3.00 additional.

$12.77 PAINTS THIS HOUSE, 24X56-22 FEET HIGH, TWO COATS.

BODY, 11 gallons No. 30Y0215 Cream { 10 gallons at 93c per gallon............$9.30
{ 1 gallon at 98c per gallon............... .98
TRIMMING, 2½ gallons No. 30Y0243 White { 2 gallons at 98c per gallon....... 1.96
{ ½ gallon for................ .53

Total.........$12.77

Roof will require 6 gallons No. 30Y800 Red Roof Paint at an additional cost of $3.65.

$8.12 PAINTS THIS HOUSE, 22X28-21 FEET HIGH, TWO COATS.

Colors and quantity of each required:

BODY, 7 gallons No. 30Y0202 Lavender { 5 gallons at 93c per gallon......$4.65
{ 2 gallons at 98c per gallon......... 1.96
TRIMMING, 1½ gallons No. 30Y0207 Lemont Stone for 1.51

Total.........$8.12

Roof will require 3 gals. No. 30Y860 Green Roof Paint at 65c per gal., $1.95 additional.

$10.53 PAINTS THIS HOUSE, 20X48-22 FEET HIGH, TWO COATS.

Colors and quantity of each required:

BODY, 9 gallons No. 30Y0221 Brown { 5 gallons at 93c per gallon..............$4.65
{ 4 gallons a 98c per gallon............ 3.92
TRIMMING, 2 gallons No 30Y0243 White at 98c per gallon................. 1.96

Total.........$10.53

Roof will require 5 gals. No. 30Y860 Green Roof Paint at 60c per gal., $3.00 additional.

16711

Introducing The Newest Dress Styles

THE fashions in frocks this season are simply bewildering, there is such variety and all are so charming. It is difficult to decide between the taffetas, the crepes, the poplins, and the plain, figured and embroidered voiles. All are indeed lovely, and we have included in our selection of dresses every material that fashion has approved. Our designs, too, are the very latest, those that Fifth Avenue is making much of in fashionable shop windows, and that New York women are wearing with great success this season. Youthfulness seems to be the dominant note, not mere girlishness, but that freshness of line and style that becomes all women. Skirts are full, much more so than last year, and sleeves are particularly pretty. Some are short, others long, and many gathered softly into cuffs and exquisitely inset with lace and embroideries. The semi-tailored dresses are not less attractive, but express this year unusual smartness. Mannish patch pockets and buttoned straps, together with ornamental stitching and perfect cut and finish, distinguish the tailored gowns, suits and blouses. We have the best of all types and at prices exceptionally low, as a glance at the following pages will demonstrate beyond a doubt. The youthfulness of this season's dress styles and their artistic beauty is perfectly expressed in our splendid assortment.

24R1310 Very exquisite is this stylish dress of handsomely embroidered voile. The panel effect in front consists of a wide band of beautiful filet pattern lace, bordered all around with handsome Cluny insertion. The Cluny is also used to trim the lower edge of the front and back yokes, and the front yoke is further ornamented with Valenciennes insertion arranged in points. The deep collar of filet pattern lace is edged with a dainty frilling of white net. A net frill, with heading of Valenciennes, is also used for the lower edge of the attractively designed sleeve. Valenciennes is arranged in pointed outline near the top of the sleeve, and the Cluny lace joins the sleeve to the embroidered cuff. The skirt is very handsomely embroidered, a band of filet pattern lace, arranged at knee depth, and below the embroidered edge a plaited flounce of plain voile is attached under a tuck finish. Fashionably full is this dainty skirt which is gathered at the top and hangs in graceful folds with stylish flare at lower edge. A girdle of satin ribbon is arranged in soft folds and finished at side front with a heading. The dress closes at left side of front panel. Sizes, 32 to 44 inches bust measure. State size.
24R1310 White with Pink Girdle.
24R1311 White with Light Blue Girdle.
24R1312 White with White Girdle. Our price.... **$4.98**

24R1310
$4.98

II

This is Mama. Her maiden name was Lillian Scott. She was born and raised in Scott Township which was named for her Grandfather Scott who was an early Pioneer in Central Iowa. Her father, my Grandpa Scott, is a lawyer, a judge, and on the State Legislature, where he is a good friend of the Governor of Iowa.

Mama attended St. Katharine's Academy in Davenport, Iowa, and taught French and Elocution at the Western Seminary in Falls City, twenty miles away from here.

Grandpa and Grandma Scott have a large farm on which they live and two other farms. Grandma Scott has Mrs. Kleinschmidt to cook and two hired girls besides. We only have Millie Flanagan who is very nice and she is Irish and goes to Mass. Her Papa is a locomotive fireman on the Northwestern Railroad. Millie is a good friend and I often help her with her work and we sometimes go to visit her married sister and take goodies to the children.

Mama is teaching Millie to cook and she is doing very well on plain cookery and will soon advance.

"Just about that time she will no doubt get married," says Papa.

Mama's dress is of handsomely embroidered voile with a panel in front of filet pattern lace bordered all around with lovely Cluny insertion.

Sometimes one or two of Mama's former students from the Western Seminary come to see her. They are grown-up ladies now and are married and one of them arrives driving her own automobile. But she only did that once as she ran onto a stump in the road on the way home and had to stay all night in a farmhouse.

7

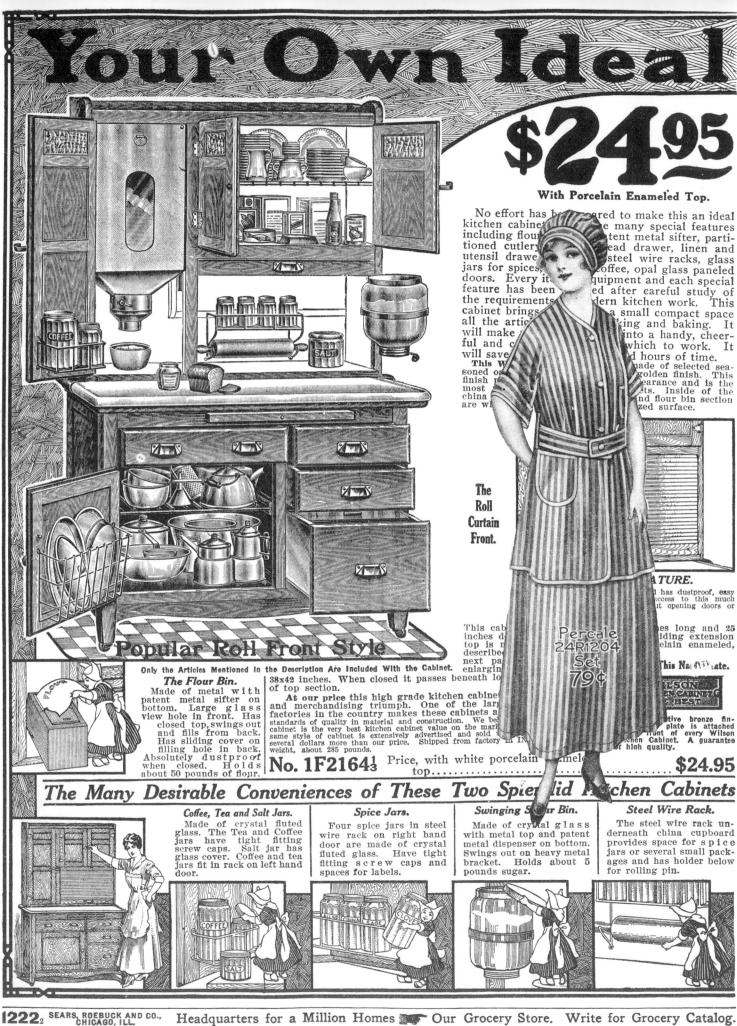

III

Great excitement today.

Papa whispered to me to stay home after lunch as he was to prepare a surprise for Mama while she was out at a card party at Aunt Charlotte's.

I was so excited I could hardly eat any lunch. "What is the matter with you, dear," said Mama. "You are scarcely eating a thing."

"I am just not very hungry today," I said but I could hardly keep from smiling.

At 2 P.M. the van from Hoffman's Furniture Store came. I ran out into the street. Papa followed. All the men said hello to Papa and he called them by name. He knows everybody in town.

"O Papa, how lovely!" I cried. "A kitchen cabinet! And such a beauty!"

"O ain't it lovely!" said Millie when the men brought it in.

"<u>Isn't</u> it lovely, please, Millie," I said.

"Yes, Miss Julia," she replied.

When Mama came home Papa and I hid in the pantry.

"Goodness gracious, Millie, where did this handsome golden oak kitchen cabinet come from?" cried Mother.

Papa and I sprang out of the pantry.

"Surprise!" we shouted gaily.

"O George, you are such a dear husband to me."

She kissed Papa right in front of Millie.

"I am glad you are pleased, Lillian," said my Father, coughing slightly.

He calls Mama "Lillian" when he is deeply moved.

Women's Stylish and Becoming Hats

16R408 $4.98

16R405 $1.79

16R411 $1.98

16R406 $3.98

16R409 $3.98

16R412 $3.98

16R407 $2.98

16R410 $2.49

16R413 $1.25

For Descriptions See Opposite Page

95

IV

Here are the teachers at Prescott Grammar School, corner of Dakota and Pike Streets, Winnebago, Iowa, in the school year of 1913–1914.

First Grade	Second Grade
Miss Bonnie Schwartz	Miss Marian Wilson

Third Grade
Miss Hilda Harnishfegger

Fourth Grade	Fifth Grade
Miss Lucy Saxton	Miss Ruth Chadwick

Sixth Grade
Miss Mavis O'Neill

Seventh Grade	Eighth Grade
Miss Ada Ramsey	Miss Anastasia Prohaska

Principal
Miss Wilma Weber

1st Grade: Miss Schwartz comes from Grant County, Wisconsin, and attended the Ladies' Seminary in Fond du Lac. She lives on Front Street and is only eighteen years old but very accomplished. She is quite in demand, as she does comic recitations and plays the "Light Cavalry Overture" on the musical water glasses.

2nd Grade: Miss Wilson is a native of Winnebago and attended Grinnell College. She lives at home. She receives visits from a young man from Des Moines.

3rd Grade: Miss Harnishfegger is the daughter of a prosperous farmer in Jackson County and is a graduate of Bayliss Business College in Dubuque. She boards with Professor Otto and his sister. She has been to Italy and has a piece of stone from the Roman Forum.

4th Grade: Miss Saxton came to Winnebago at an early age from North

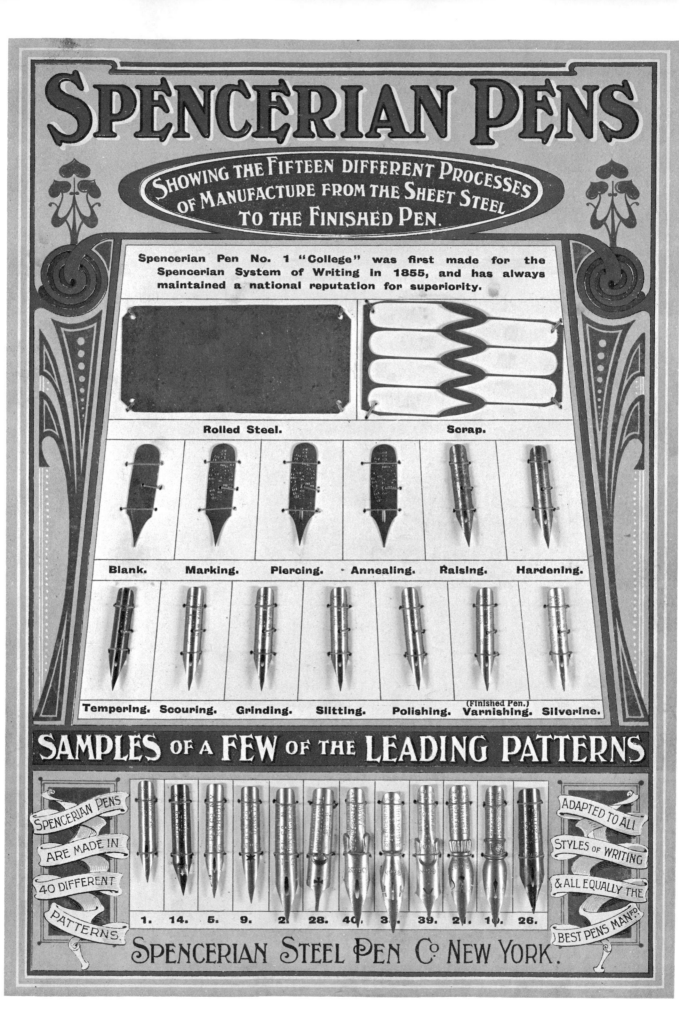

SPENCERIAN PENS

SHOWING THE FIFTEEN DIFFERENT PROCESSES OF MANUFACTURE FROM THE SHEET STEEL TO THE FINISHED PEN.

Spencerian Pen No. 1 "College" was first made for the Spencerian System of Writing in 1855, and has always maintained a national reputation for superiority.

Rolled Steel.   Scrap.

Blank.   Marking.   Piercing.   Annealing.   Raising.   Hardening.

Tempering. Scouring.   Grinding.   Slitting.   Polishing. (Finished Pen.) Varnishing.   Silverine.

SAMPLES OF A FEW OF THE LEADING PATTERNS

SPENCERIAN PENS ARE MADE IN 40 DIFFERENT PATTERNS.

ADAPTED TO ALL STYLES OF WRITING & ALL EQUALLY THE BEST PENS MAN'F'D

1.   14.   5.   9.   2.   28.   40.   3.   39.   21.   10.   26.

SPENCERIAN STEEL PEN CO. NEW YORK.

Dakota. She is plump and jolly and a moving spirit in many activities both in and out of school.

5th Grade: Miss Chadwick was born in Rockingham Junction, New Hampshire. She attended the Robinson Female Seminary in Exeter, New Hampshire, and the State of New Hampshire Normal School. She came West last year when her father opened a law office here. She pronounces English with what Papa calls a "rube" accent.

6th Grade: Miss Mavis O'Neill is from our neighbor state of Missouri. She is said to have had an unfortunate love affair in East St. Louis. She has been here in town for four years and is engaged to young Doctor Kingsbury.

7th Grade: Miss Ada Ramsey is a native of our town and her father is Clerk of the Court. She is considered the prettiest girl in town and keeps company with Johnny Bretschneider, who unfortunately owns the Pastime Pool Hall.

8th Grade: Miss Anastasia Prohaska was born and raised in Oxford Mills, Iowa, in Cedar County. She is a graduate of the State University of Iowa in Iowa City. She is an inspiring teacher and a good friend.

Principal: Miss Weber our principal is rather old. She is 33 years of age and has been engaged to Walter Randall, Papa's head clerk at the EMPORIUM, for nine years. She rules the school with a firm hand. She lives with her mother who is an old crabapple.

PALACE WINDSOR HEATER

A Big, Capable, Full Nickel Trimmed, Handsomely Carved, Self-Feeding, Double Heating Hard Coal or Crushed Coke Base Burner

Is as pleasing in appearance as it is useful and economical

An old favorite that has successfully kept thousands of homes warm and comfortable in the coldest weather. Test it in your own home. No matter what price you are willing to pay for a heater, none will give you longer or more satisfactory service than our Palace Windsor. It represents full heating value for every dollar of cost and means a saving of a full third on the purchase price alone. It will give you better, more economical, more reliable, and longer-wearing service than other heating stoves often sold at from $10.00 to $20.00 more than our low, economy prices. You can have a Big Fire or a Small Fire, just according to the weather conditions: Your Heater is always under perfect control; therefore your fuel bill is smaller than it would be with less carefully constructed Heaters. Each and every Palace Windsor Heater is perfect in every detail. Read carefully our full description of this heater given on opposite page. Our improved shipping facilities means only a small amount of freight added to our money-saving price. You could not make a better or more satisfactory heater purchase.

Shipped promptly from Foundry near Buffalo, N. Y.

We ship from the point nearest you. In that way the freight charges will be reduced to a minimum and your stove will reach you in the shortest possible time.

See Next Page for Complete Details of Special Palace Windsor Features

The Palace Windsor Perfect

(7) Strong, Durable Dampers, and Damper Handles.
(8) Convenient Tea Kettle Heating Top.
(9) Large Swell Front, with Mica Doors all the way around.
(10) Large Nickel Plated Reflector Dome.
(11) Elegant Design, heavy nickel finish.
(12) Sold on a Guarantee that makes Satisfaction Sure.

Full Description of this Heater given on opposite page

Prices for Palace Windsor Heater, nicely blackened and polished, securely crated.

Article No.	Price	Stove No.	Diameter of Fire Pot Inches Outside	Inside	Floor Space Inches	Smoke Pipe Inches	Hot Air Pipe Inches	Height Floor to Top of Urn. In.	Average Shipping Weight Pounds
268B2611	$27.75	213	13½	12	25x25	6	7	66¾	405
268B2612	31.50	215	16	14	27x27	6	7	67¾	470
268B2613	37.25	217	18	16	29x29	6	7	69¾	540

Shipped from foundry near Buffalo, N. Y.

V

Here is a riddle Mama made up:

"When is a house a palace?"
Answer: "When it has a Palace base burner in it."

This is our Palace Windsor anthracite base burner that keeps us warm and cozy. It is very beautiful and trimmed in nickel silver with little windows through which the fire glows cheerily. On very cold mornings we are allowed to come downstairs and dress by the stove.

It feeds hard coal through a hopper at the top and burns all night.

I think our base burner is the most beautiful on the street. My friend Harriet Hackenbush has an Art Garland that she thinks is prettier than our Palace Windsor but I do not agree. I don't have to agree with her on everything just because she is my best friend.

Millie keeps the black iron parts shiny with Black Silk Stove Polish and she keeps the little windows clean with vinegar.

We have three other stoves:

In the kitchen we have a big Glenwood six-hole range with hot water reservoir, warming closet, and oven thermometer. It burns hard or soft coal, coke, wood, or corn cobs. There is a hot water boiler attached so we have lovely hot water in the kitchen as well as the upstairs bathroom.

In the dining room is an Acme Oak, a very pretty little stove but one of the grates is burnt which makes Papa quite angry at times.

Upstairs in Mama and Papa's bedroom is a Victory Hot Blast Wood Burner. It is not much fun because it has no windows in it.

Grandpa Scott has a furnace in his house of course, but I do not envy him. Although perhaps Papa does. I am sure my brother Arnold does, as it is his task to fill the hopper and the hods with coal and take out the ash pan. On Saturday mornings it is worse, for he has to sift the ashes out by the barn and pick out the unburnt pieces of anthracite.

As for myself I think there is nothing so homelike as to come into the house on a bitter wintry day and receive a warm welcome from the big beautiful glowing base burner.

If you had a furnace you would have to go down in the cellar and stand by the furnace which would be no fun at all. Besides, furnaces are very ugly and there are probably mice in the basement and who likes mice? I certainly don't.

BLACK HAMBURGH.

SILVER-PENCILLED HAMBURGH.

BROWN-BREASTED RED GAME COCK.

FORWARD, MARCH

ALLEN & GINTER'S
CIGARETTES
RICHMOND, VIRGINIA

10B4010
Serge
$225

OFFICER OF THE DAY

ALLEN & GINTER'S
CIGARETTES
RICHMOND, VIRGINIA

CARRY ARMS

ALLEN & GINTER'S
CIGARETTES
RICHMOND, VIRGINIA

READY

ALLEN &
GINTER'S   CIGARETTES
RICHMOND, VIRGINIA

MANY HORNS.
BLACKFEET SIOUX.

RED CLOUD.
DAKOTA SIOUX.

KEOKUK.
SAC & FOX.

DEER HAM.
IOWAY.

VI

Mostly all of the young people here in Winnebago have "collections." Of course I collect cigar bands and box labels, whereas my brother Arnold collects birds' nests, plug tobacco tags, and postage stamps. He doesn't collect the birds' nests until the nesting season is over I am glad to say. Katie Sheridan has over 600 different picture postcards and Fatty Clark's collection at present consists of 1,263 postmarks from all over the U.S.A. and Canada.

My girl chum Harriet has one of the prettiest collections in town. The last time we counted she had 912 cigarette cards. With every package of ten cigarettes there is a free picture card. She gets them from her oldest brother, Eldon, who works in the bank, from her Uncle in Sheboygan, and from another Uncle in Lowell, Mass.

There are many, many subjects of these pretty cards, such as Actresses, Flags of All Nations, College Pennants, Battleships, Presidents, Baseball Players, Military Uniforms, Embarrassing Moments, Automobiles, Comics, and so on and so forth.

The picture shows Harriet with a few of her cards.

At the top are some very rare cards called "Fifty Prize and Game Chickens." Harriet has only nine of these and despairs of ever completing the set. Grandpa Scott has two beautiful Black Hamburghs out on the farm like the one on the left. There was a Silver-Pencilled Hamburgh at the County Fair. Mr. Sullivan who owns the Livery Stable has three Game Cocks similar to the bird on the right. Arnold says he takes them to Falls City and fights them.

The four ladies surrounding Harriet in their rather quaint dress are from a large set with the name "Parasol Drill." It is all very frivolous and silly I think, but not as silly as the Language of Flowers, which is another set and too absurd for words. From top left the ladies represent "Forward March," "Carry Arms," "Ready," and "Officer of the Day."

The Indians at the bottom are from a much-prized set and are considered highly dramatic and artistically depicted.

You will notice Chief Keokuk with the necklace of bear claws. My grandfather Harrington met Chief Keokuk in 1845 when the Sac Indians were moved by the U.S. Government from Iowa across the Missouri to what is now Kansas. Grandpa Harrington was raised at the Indian Agency at the forks of the Raccoon and Des Moines rivers and spoke the Sac and Fox tongue like English. His father was a trader and had a log cabin store and this livelihood has come

17

Will be home soon

803

WHAT MADE THE BOYS LIKE ROSIE

Arrived Safely With My Luggage At WELLS

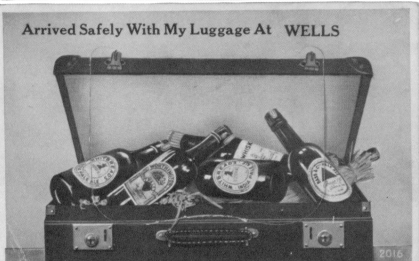

2016

STEAMER DUBUQUE
Dubuque. Iowa. U.S.A.

WHY DON'T YOU PHONE ME, HAVE YOU FORGOTTEN MY NUMBER?

605-6

Pennsylvania R. R. under the Hudson River, New York City.

down in the family; Papa is also a trader, only he owns the EMPORIUM, which has electric lights and a cash trolley that runs up and down and along the ceiling to and from the cashier up on a balcony.

The Sac and Fox are still in Iowa, on the reservation at Tama of 3,253.76 acres which they bought and paid for with their own money, the only such reservation in the U.S.A. Nowadays they call themselves the Meskwaki and their chief in the year 1913 is called Pushetonikwa.

Papa took me and my brother Arnold to the Pow Wow which is every August in Tama. I shook hands with the chief. Papa told him that my grandfather had been a friend of the great Chief Keokuk. Pushetonikwa was pleased and gave me an eagle feather with a thong on it.

So these are a few highlights of the famed Harriet Hackenbush Cigarette Card Treasury and you can see why we enjoy it so much.

And just to be fair, here are some thrilling and entertaining samples of some of Katie Sheridan's more unusual picture postcards. Thanks, Katie!

VII

"Don't forget to drink your milk, dear," Mama said.

"It's good for your bones," Papa said.

"O I don't care about my old bones," I said. "Pearl's milk tastes so udgy. Why can't we get our milk out of nice bottles like Harriet's family?"

"Harry Hackenbush," said Papa, "has been putting on airs since we were both in the Third Grade out in Winneshiek Township."

"O Mama, do we have to keep a cow?" I said.

"It's one of your father's fancies," said Mama.

"But Mama, this is nineteen thirteen," I said.

"If it was nineteen sixty-six," Papa said, helping himself to about five more buckwheat cakes and some pork sausages, "we would still keep a cow. It is a settling influence. And besides, she gives milk."

"But Pearl's milk is absolutely udgy!" I said.

"That will be enough in that vein from you, Miss Pert," said Papa.

Well guess what? That evening Pearl drank most of a pail of kerosene that Vernon the hired man had left in the barn. This will show you how ignorant a cow can be and Pearl is probably the most ignorant of the entire bovine world population.

The next day she was sick and so sick that she sweated drops of kerosene oil. Vernon milked her and kerosene spots formed on the milk. None of us would drink her milk after that so Papa sold her to a farmer out beyond the butter tub factory. Papa told the farmer about the kerosene but the farmer didn't believe it.

I was very happy and told Harriet I supposed at last we would get our milk from the Perfection Dairy in nice bottles like civilized people. But O dear! Two days later Papa bought a new cow from a farmer out at Simpson's Furnace named Ethel. O what a perfectly ridiculous name for a cow.

We are still choking down udgy milk.

Papas are so stubborn.

21

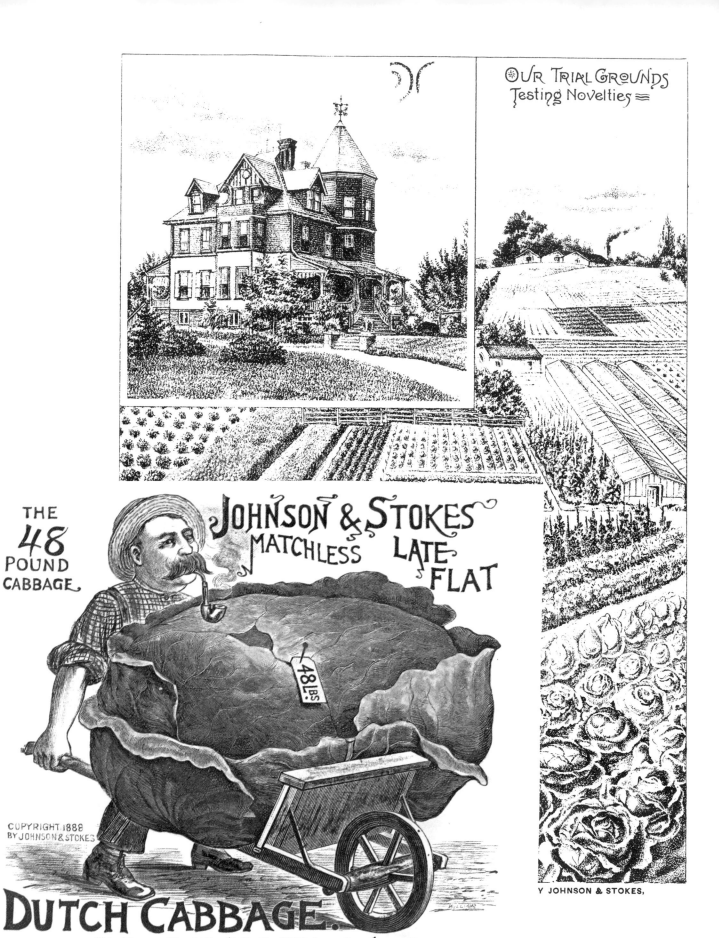

VIII

This is Grandpa Scott's house in Scott Township. It is six miles from Winnebago on the State Road.

I guess Grandpa has about the biggest vegetable garden in the world. Last year he sent a Dutch cabbage to the Iowa State Fair that weighed 48 pounds. He won.

The best part in summer is to sit on the big shady porch in the afternoon and play games. Mrs. Kleinschmidt the cook sends out lemonade with ice tinkling in it, and Bertha brings out cookies. She is one of Grandma's maids and is 16 years old and very plump. Grandma pays her three dollars a week and I heard Papa say to Mama, "Your mother is spoiling those girls blind. There is nobody in this town who pays their girl more than two and a half dollars a week."

Grandma's parlor has plush draperies and a grand piano from Germany. I always bring my music when I come out to Scottdale, as the farm is called. Grandma and Grandpa like to hear me play. Sometimes Grandma and Mama play duets, which has a serious effect on Grandpa who has a great deal of emotion. When they are through he has to blow his nose and wipe his eyes. It is even worse when Grandma and I play duets.

On the third floor of the mansion is the billiard room. Sometimes my friend Harriet Hackenbush and I are invited out for a day and a night and don't we have fun in the billiard room on a rainy day, or especially in winter when there is a blizzard just swirling around the eaves and those cute dormer windows in the roof. Occasionally my girl cousins come from Falls City and we have such fun you can't imagine. We make fudge or pull taffy and play billiards and slide on the banisters and tease Mrs. Kleinschmidt (just in fun you know) and at night we have pillow fights. I don't imagine anyone in the United States or even the world has as much fun as we have in Winnebago and at Grandpa's farm. I don't suppose I will have so much fun when I grow up. I am not particularly anxious to grow up yet. But I suppose I will have to, whether I like it or not.

We have buckwheat cakes and sausages for breakfast on the farm and Grandpa sometimes has <u>steak</u>, <u>fried</u> <u>potatoes</u>, and <u>apple pie</u> for breakfast.

My main ambition in life is to have a house like Grandpa's at Scottdale.

Big Stockings Full of Toys and Candy

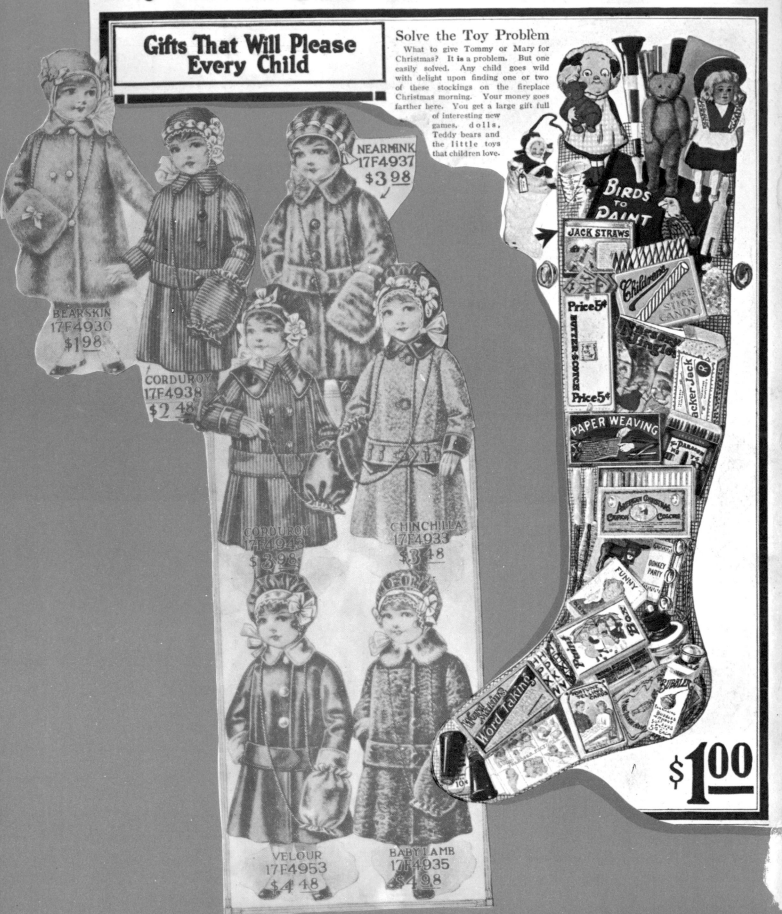

Gifts That Will Please Every Child

Solve the Toy Problem

What to give Tommy or Mary for Christmas? It **is** a problem. But one easily solved. Any child goes wild with delight upon finding one or two of these stockings on the fireplace Christmas morning. Your money goes farther here. You get a large gift full of interesting new games, dolls, Teddy bears and the little toys that children love.

BEARSKIN
17F4930
$1.98

CORDUROY
17F4938
$2.48

NEARMINK
17F4937
$3.98

CORDUROY
17F4943
$3.98

CHINCHILLA
17F4933
$3.48

VELOUR
17F4953
$4.48

BABY LAMB
17F4935
$4.98

BIRDS TO PAINT

JACK STRAWS

Price 5¢ BUTTER-SCOTCH Price 5¢

Childrens PURE STICK CANDY

Cracker Jack

PAPER WEAVING

DONKEY PARTY

FUNNY

BUBBLER

Word Making Word Taking

$1.00

IX

O to be in Iowa, now that Christmas is here! We had a lovely snowfall on the 19th and the sound of sleigh bells fills the air. Racy cutters with their smartly curved dashboards in highly polished red or green vie for position with the big bobsleds from the lumberyard. Everywhere in the crisp pure air sounds the music of the big Swedish sleigh bells, the open shaft bells, the gong shaft bells, the pole and saddle chimes, and the entrancing silvery Russian saddle chimes. Everybody has got their genuine buffalo or shiny plush robes out of mothballs. Meanwhile the automobiles go puffing about blowing steam most amazingly and clanking their tire chains in the snowy streets.

It is a perfect time of year, everyone is in such jolly spirits, and even grumpy old Mr. Biggs the cobbler gave Harriet two cigarette cards when we went in to pick up her Papa's congress boots. He even managed a smile. "Quite unheard of," as Mama says. I can't imagine how he knew Harriet collected them.

It is very cold and the train whistles have a different frosty freezing tone. Walking down the street your shoes make squeaky noises on the packed snow. Jack Frost has worked his artistry on windowpanes. Noses are rather red and all the feminine band are carrying their muffs. Small boys and girls are wound around and around with scarves so that only their peeping eyes can be seen between scarf and knitted cap.

The stores look very pretty this year. Papa's EMPORIUM is trimmed with tinsel garlands, imitation holly vines, and large red tissue-paper bells. Potterveld's Drug Store has two large palmetto palms in the windows and artificial poinsettias. The palms are dried in a special way and keep forever. Harriet's Papa's "Oriental Sweet Shoppe" has pennants spelling "Merry Christmas" and red festooning.

It is fun to go into the EMPORIUM and see everybody carefully picking out gifts for their loved ones. (Also for the ones they don't love but have to give presents to!) I tell you the cash trolleys are really whizzing. Business is so brisk that Papa is waiting on trade right alongside Walter, Fanny, Emily, Mrs. Kowalski, and all the other clerks.

Of course there was an entertainment at school on the last day. I was one of the "Wise Men" as usual. I do believe that if I ran away from home to New York and became an actress I would end up on Broadway as a "Wise Man."

25

A MERRY CHRISTMAS

A happy Christmas

"THINE OWN WISH WISH"

Merry Christmas.

A Merry Christmas Papa from Julia

A MERRY CHRISTMAS

I assisted at the party for the children in the Second Presbyterian Church vestry, but for the first time "Santa" had not left a gift for me. "You're a young lady now, Julia," said horrid old skinny Mrs. Coots. I confess I went into the cloak room to hide my tears. I was too proud after that to take the customary gay little box of hard candy. I gave mine to little Lucy Dubois.

O well, "Say la vee," as Papa says, which is French and means "That's life for you."

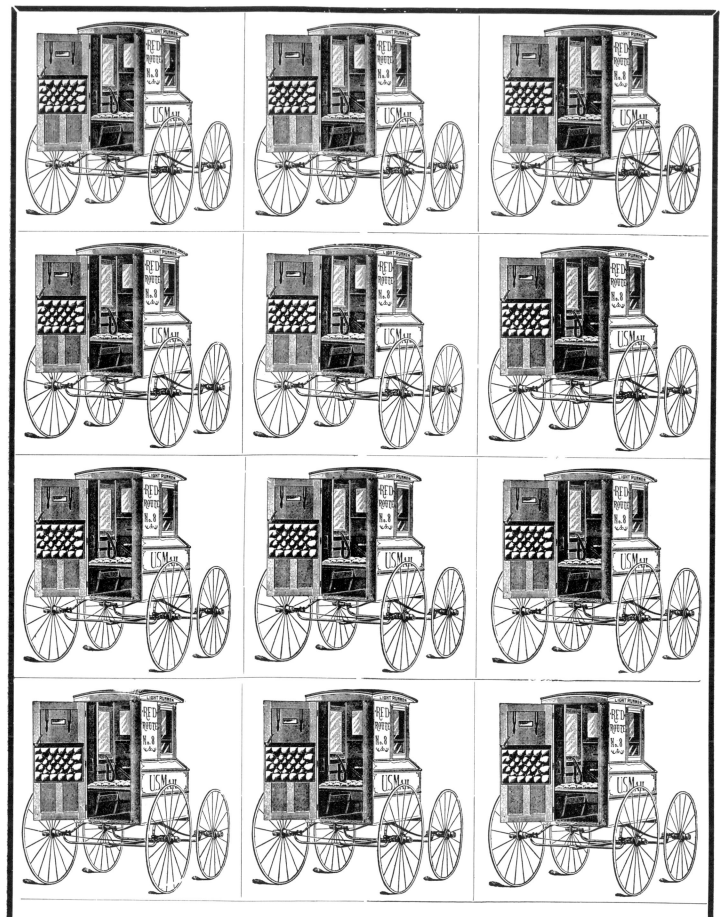

We make Mail Wagons. Send for our New 20-page catalogue

HARRINGTON MFG. CO. = = = PEORIA, ILLINOIS

X

O I have been so sick.

Mama has been sitting with me and I have had gruel and milk toast.

Millie Flanagan has been a dear and comes to sit with me so Mama can get some rest. She tells me stories.

Doctor Sears came to see me yesterday and he gave me some pills.

At eleven A.M. Millie went to the kitchen to get me a cup custard and I heard Mr. Pugsley the mailman coming down the street through the snow with his sleigh bells. I wanted to see his new horse so much.

Mr. Pugsley has two broncos and one road horse. Papa sat with me last night and told me Mr. Pugsley had one of his broncos die last month of bad feed. Papa told me he had a new real Western bronco; it was broke in Nebraska and came in on the last cattle train on the Northwestern. His name is Gunhammer. I wanted so much to see him if he was drawing today.

I went to the window from my bed. It was snowing hard.

I saw the mail wagon.

It was the effect of those horrid pills Doctor Sears gave me. I was all dizzy.

I saw a dozen mail wagons.

I was standing at the window when Millie came back.

"Saints above, Miss Julia!" she cried, and got me back to bed.

"I wanted to see Gunhammer," I said.

"Gunhammer!" she cried, "What's Gunhammer? Lord help us, she's delirious!" And she ran off to get Mama.

By nightfall when Papa arrived home from the store I was much better and ate a nice lamb chop. I told Papa about Gunhammer and seeing all the mail wagons and he laughed and laughed.

The snow has stopped and the temperature has gone to 26 degrees below zero. Papa is busy with the stoves and says:

"One of these days I am going to have a furnace put in this blankety-blank house."

$225.00 Our Windsor Concert Grand Upright Piano $225.00

A Model of Artistic Beauty, richly finished and possesses a tone of great depth and brilliancy. A piano for which no apologies will ever be necessary. Sold under our liberal terms and binding guarantee as the peer, from every standpoint of pianos sold by the regular dealers at double our price.

The beautiful piano illustrated on this page is our new style Concert Grand Upright, and it is not only the finest instrument we have ever been able to offer but is one of the most exquisitely designed and artistically constructed pianos in the American market to-day. In appearance it is a model of artistic beauty; the ornamentation is richly executed and the finish is superb. In other words it is a strictly high grade artistic piano made under the personal supervision of an expert builder of over 30 years' experience, and in durability, quality, and sustaining power of tone, they are as good as money, skill, and experience can produce; in fact every detail is in keeping with the highest priced modern pianos. If you are ready to purchase a piano, permit us to send you one of these superb instruments on 30 days' approval (see introductory page). You are under no obligations to keep the piano if it is not as represented or does not in every way please you. All we ask is the privilege of shipping you one and are willing to rely on your own judgment as to its merits. Don't hesitate to ask the opinion of the best musicians in your town as to the quality.

Description of our Windsor Concert Grand Piano

THE CASE is all hardwood double veneered inside and out with selected figured American walnut or San Domingo Mahogany Veneers; massively constructed ends with large rounded corners, deep ornamental moulding around top, heavy lid with neatly chiseled edges, solid pilasters handsomely carved, full swing front music desk with highly polished center panel surrounded by artistically [car]ved scroll patterns, rich[ly orn]amented with beaded [mould]ings, double rolling [fall bo]ard, extra heavy [leg]s and foundation [boar]d. The latter with oval [shap]ed edges, double [hand] artistically [carved] and gracefully taper[ed]. [D]ouble lower panels, [with] deep beaded mould[ings]. Base finished with heavy mouldings. Continu[ou]s nickel-plated hinges on [the ... nickel-] [plated ped]als

6W11612

$168 Flannel

of [quality ...] [a per]ce. We [two] coats of [v]arnish, [r]ubbed [in]ol.

Serge 6W11612X

98¢

Crepe de Chine
700R $25.00

The [...]indsor Concert Grand Upright Piano. Dimensions: height, 4 ft. 8 in [...] 2 ft 4 in.

TONE. In th[...] considered, but a[...] It matters not [...] of an inferior c[...] is in this resp[...] really high grade piano is easily recognized, e[...] [...]h the low priced commercial instruments kno[...] [...] latter are not made for tone; they are m[...] [...]ich tone quality in the highest degree; [...]est judges in Chicago, also by hundreds [...]rom every possible standpoint. [...] of our piano is that it does not require

[...]re, of course, many points to be carefully [...] is the tone. [...] how elaborate the finish, if the tone is [...] worthless as a musical instrument. It an expert to demonstrate its purity. [...]even by a novice, instantly reveals i[...] for itself. Every purchaser of a [...] is perfect before final acceptance. full thirty days' trial of our instr[...] have an opportunity to amply test it[...] of our strong recommendation we do If you are not satisfied to rely up[...] or any part of the construction of ou[...] best musicians in your town. We hav[...] willing and anxious to submit it on competent judge.

[...]fingers over the keys, [...]uality which speaks [...] that the tone [...] that we allow [...] this time you [...] itself worthy

tonal quality [...] [s]ervices of the [...]ndsor and are [...] [...]o the careful scrutiny of any honest,

OUR GUARANTEE.

Every Windsor piano is warranted for ten years from date of shipment. If at any time within ten years any imperfections develop, either in material or workmanship, we hereby agree to repair it free of all charge. Should it be necessary to forward same to our factory, we pay freight both ways.

LF120—Windsor pianos as shown and described above, 7¼ octaves, overstrung scale, double repeating action, three strings tuned in unison throughout the treble polished iron frame including fine stool, complete instruction book and scarf. Weight, boxed, about 850 lb. Each, F.O.B. Chicago............$225.00

XI

Every Friday when school is out at 4 P.M. I go directly to my music lesson on Elm Street at Miss Wilhelmina Otto's. She lives in a nice cottage on the corner with her brother, Professor Otto, who teaches music, voice, orchestra and band at the college. They are Germans — I mean they come from Germany — they are Americans now. But they have a big picture of the king of Germany, Kaiser Wilhelm the Second, over their sofa as well as a picture of the German royal family over the piano. There is also a large framed certificate of Professor Otto's service in the German Army. All very lovely but can you imagine, there is also a photograph of a dead person in a coffin surrounded by flowers who Miss Egstrand the seamstress says is the Ottos' dead brother. I try not to look at this.

Miss Otto is a very good piano teacher and Mama says, "O Miss Otto, you are bringing our Julia along just beautifully."

"Chulia iss a vine bupil," says Miss Otto. She talks like that.

"Vell, Chulia, vare you vass?" Papa says when I come home from my lesson. "Bist du bei Fräulein Hohenzollern gewesen?"

Papa talks German because he was raised in New Vienna, Iowa, where, he says, "If you didn't talk German when I was a lad you wouldn't have anyone to talk to."

Miss Otto can't help telling me about how much nicer everything is in Germany. She says everybody in Germany is so artistic and intellectual.

"Yes," says Papa when I tell him that. "Especially the Krupp iron works. And the Death's Head Hussars — they're terribly artistic, I hear."

"Now George," says Mama, "don't start on that."

We have a Windsor Concert Grand upright piano of selected San Domingo Mahogany veneers, the whole of it richly ornamented. Miss Otto says the tone is very good "for an American piano." Poor dear, she can't help it.

My friend Harriet takes violin from Professor Otto.

"Harriet is a very sweet girl," Mama said the other day, "but I don't think the violin is her instrument."

"O yes it is, Mama," I said. "Her Papa paid sixty-four dollars for it."

Mama explained what she meant and I think she is right.

Poor Miss Otto. Being homesick is so dreadful. I had it when I went to Storm Lake for three days one time. O it was awful.

31

CUPID & Co. ♡

Variety of HEARTS for SALE.

BARGAIN DAY
Feb. 14

My Valentine.

I bought a heart, tender and true,
And now I find it's thine,
I cannot give it back to you,
But ask you to take mine.

XII

February 14, 1914
St. Valentine's Day.

This special day goes back to Roman times when there was a Festival called the Lupercalia, except it was on February 15th and they didn't have valentines.

In the Middle Ages a man or a boy could kiss the first person he met on February 14th. I can't imagine how <u>that</u> worked out. Suppose the first person he met going down the street was somebody horrid like skinny old Mrs. Coots, or old crabapple Mrs. Weber, our principal's mother? Suppose he met Ada Ramsey and kissed her? Wouldn't her fiancé Johnny Bretschneider punch him in the nose?

Valentines were invented in the 19th Century along with the cotton gin, the sewing machine and McCormick's reaper.

I received fourteen valentines today. This is my prettiest one.

I suspect it is from Papa, unless I have a very ardent secret admirer, as it cost 25 cents. I know because I saw it at the Variety Store.

FAME
No 170.   5 Cents.

AND
FORTUNE WEEKLY.

STORIES OF BOYS WHO MAKE MONEY.

BANKER BARRY'S BOY;
OR, GATHERING THE DOLLARS IN WALL STREET.
BY A SELF-MADE MAN.

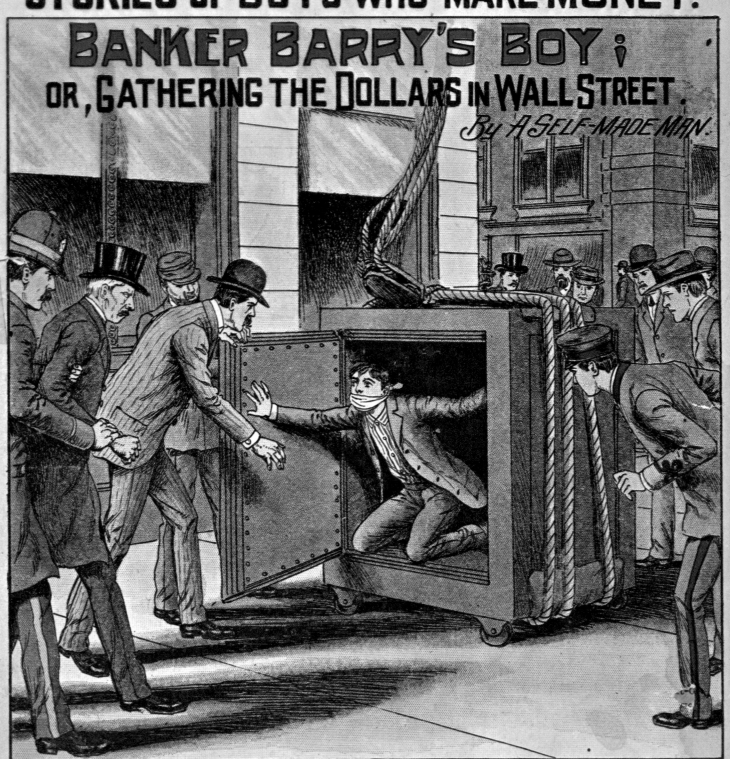

As the safe touched the sidewalk Broker Barry heard muffled sounds coming from its interior. The door was not tightly closed, so he swung it open. To his amazement, he beheld Bob Honner, his messenger boy, gagged and half suffocated.

XIII

My brother Arnold is always trading dime novels and nickel newspapers with his chums especially Fatty Clark. He doesn't mind being called Fatty, as his real name is Melvin. My chum Harriet has a case on him but she denies it.

Mama does not approve. She says these papers are trashy and give "false impressions of life."

Millie Flanagan, our girl, also incurs Mama's displeasure in her choice of reading material. She has a new book every week from her married sister, Mrs. Patrick O'Neill, whose husband is our leading blacksmith in town. Last week she had **Sweet Love's Atonement** by Mrs. E.D.E.N. Southworth and this week she has been reading **Lady Viola's Secret** by Bertha M. Clay. Mother has tried to get her to read **Ivanhoe** but this was a total failure and the same with **Dombey and Son** by Charles Dickens.

Saturday, Arnold traded his copy of **The Haunted Sloop; or, On and Off Soundings** for a **Fame and Fortune Weekly,** the title being **Banker Barry's Boy; or, Gathering the Dollars in Wall Street.** I read it Sunday evening when Mama and Papa were at a whist party and it is very exciting and instructive. The only thing being, these papers are traded around among the boys so much that the copy was quite shabby. It told of a boy named Bob Honner who was rewarded $5,000 by Mr. Barry for "foiling two crooks" and out of that money he made $100,000 in only a year in the diamond market. He also married Bessie Bowker, daughter of Captain Bowker. But this is only a particle of the plot which is very intricate.

Mama brought the subject up again at supper last night. It was liver and onions on Papa's account which I can't even eat. So I ate a lot of everything else, mostly hot biscuits.

Papa said, "Well, Lily, let us give these controversial literary effusions a fair trial. You and I will sit as a Court of Enquiry. You shall read and report your findings on Millie's latest romance, while I delve into the pluck and luck division. Arnold, what have you to offer in the inspirational line?"

Arnold said he would give Papa **Banker Barry's Boy** and also **Dick Merriwell's Flying Tackle.** I don't care much for the Merriwell stories. I find Dick and Frank Merriwell rather too well satisfied with themselves.

"Fair enough," said Papa, and when Millie came in with the dessert which was Floating Island Pudding he said, "Millie, have you a novel this week from

LADY VIOLA'S SECRET

BY

Bertha M. Clay

your sister, Mrs. O'Neill?'' and she said yes, she had **Lady Viola's Secret** by Bertha M. Clay. Papa asked her if she would lend it to Mama to read.

"Only to see if it is suitable reading for a young girl under my roof," said Mama hastily.

"O Missus, it's very suitable," said Millie, "it's all about Lords and Ladies and Dukes and hunting them poor little foxes on horseback and society balls among the high-ups."

After supper Papa went to his lodge meeting and Arnold and I did our lessons and went to bed.

After school the next day Harriet and Katie Sheridan and I strolled down to town. We dropped into Papa's store, the EMPORIUM, to see the new yard goods which had just come in. And then we surprised Papa in his office. It was quite a surprise because he was at his big roll-top desk reading **Banker Barry's Boy.**

"Well, girls, you have caught me red-handed," he said, and gave us each a dime for a soda. Katie and I had chocolate. Harriet, who prides herself on being "different," had raspberry.

When I got home Mama was sitting in the bay window reading **Lady Viola's Secret.** Mama was crying and dabbing her eyes with her pocket handkerchief.

"O poor Lady Viola! O that wicked monster, Lord Castlemaine!" cried Mama with a sob.

XIV

Pa, Uncle Ed, and Mr. Hinckley went out to look at the train wreck. Number 18 westbound was derailed and over thirty boxcars are all piled up in a jumble.

"I wish you would not go out there on such a cold day, dear," said Mama looking at the thermometer which said 13 below zero.

"Don't worry, Lil," said Papa. "I'll wear my Russian dog-skin fur coat and my Detroit-style genuine sealskin cap."

"I think those Russians are horrid to make men's coats out of dogs," I said.

"Well, well," he replied. "Your fur hat and muff that you are so fond of are made out of bunny rabbits. What do you say to that?"

"O," I said. "I don't even want to think about it. You're a horrid Papa."

Pretty soon Mr. Hinckley arrived in his automobile to go out to see the wreck. He owns the implement store and also sells automobiles. We were relieved to see that he and Uncle Ed both had on their fur coats.

They got out to the wreck of Number 18 at 1:30 P.M. and stayed until 3:00 P.M. A big steam crane from Council Bluffs was clearing the boxcars. Nobody got hurt in the wreck because the derailing was in the middle of the train which had 128 cars.

When they got back to the automobile it would not start. It was too cold. They joked Mr. Hinckley about it.

"Well George, this is pretty bad advertising for the Haynes automobile," Papa said. "Especially with this crowd here."

"Yes George," said Uncle Ed. "I guess when I buy my new car I will get a Franklin from Jim Funk over in Falls City."

But Mr. Hinckley did not laugh much.

"I didn't know Ed was going to buy an automobile," said Mama as Papa related the above at dinner.

"He isn't. It was just a joke, dear," said Papa.

"Oh," said Mama.

Finally they got a ride home with Johnny Bretschneider who had his big bobsleigh out there. He had his sweetheart Miss Ada Ramsey with him.

"I don't know how that jughead Ramsey got such a beautiful daughter," Pa said.

"Have some more dumplings," said Mama.

No. 5578 Outside $12.00 per M. Net.
No. 5579 Inside $24.00 per M. Net.
ALSO BLANK.

GEO. S. HARRIS & SONS,
19th St. and 4th Ave., New York.
108-110 Randolph St., Chicago.
723 Bryant St., San Francisco.

SMOKE LETTER BOX CIGARS

No. 5594 Outside $11.00 per M. Net.
No. 5595 Inside $22.00 per M. Net.
ALSO BLANK.

GEO. S. HARRIS & SONS,
19th St. and 4th Ave., New York.
108-110 Randolph St., Chicago.
723 Bryant St., San Francisco.

XV

Grandpa Scott saves cigar boxes for me. I steam the pictures off the lids with Millie's help and paste them in a scrapbook. Don't you think that is an unusual hobby for a girl?

As Grandpa is in the State Legislature people give him cigars to be friendly and when he has smoked them he gives me the box. I even have some cigar box pictures from the Governor of Iowa himself! It's true.

Grandpa was in the Governor's office one day in the State Capitol Building in Des Moines, Iowa, when the Governor said to him, "Henry, I am swamped here with cigars. Do me a favor and take a half-dozen boxes with you."

Around here everybody calls Grandpa "Judge Scott" but the Governor of our glorious state of Iowa calls him by his first name.

"Most of these cigars are pretty bad," the Governor added.

"Yes," said Grandpa. "And you've observed, of course, that the gaudier the box top the more unspeakable the cigars."

The Governor laughed.

Grandpa gave me two boxes from the Governor.

One was called "Letter Box" and had a lady in a big lavender hat posting a letter.

The other was the most peculiar cigar box I ever did see. The cigar brand was "The Style" and the picture was of a fancy lady and gentleman in a funny automobile carriage with a coachman on the box. There was a big building in the back called Waldorf Astoria which Papa says is the best hotel in New York.

Well, I took the cigars out and put them in a paper bag from Helbings' Grocery and told Millie to give them to her father, the railroad fireman on the Northwestern.

Just imagine, a few days later Harriet and Bessie Gale and I went down to the depot after school to see Number 6 and say hello to Mr. Flanagan.

He was leaning out of the locomotive cab and smoking a cigar. Mr. Clark the engineer crossed the cab and he was smoking a cigar. They thanked me for the cigars and we girls strolled down the train and the baggageman was smoking a cigar, the conductor was smoking a cigar, the brakeman was smoking a cigar, and even the candy butcher, skinny old Charlie Harper, was smoking a cigar.

Everybody on the whole train crew of Number 6 was smoking either a "Letter Box" or a "The Style" cigar!

"That's what I smoke!"

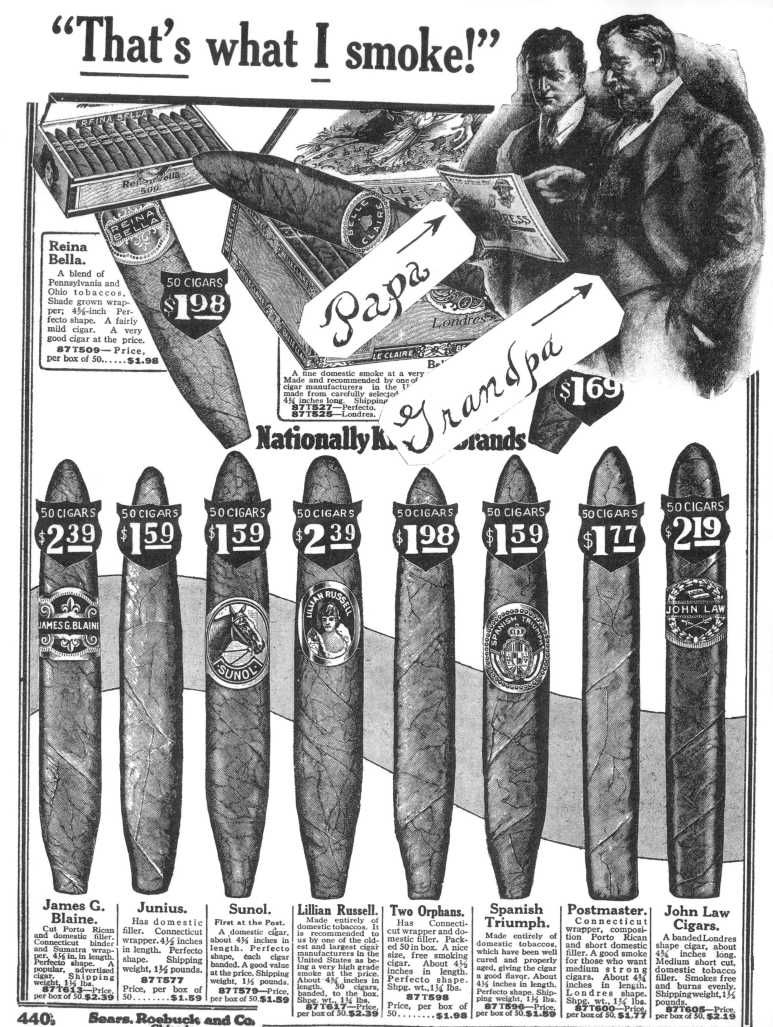

Reina Bella.
A blend of Pennsylvania and Ohio tobaccos. Shade grown wrapper; 4⅝-inch Perfecto shape. A fairly mild cigar. A very good cigar at the price.
87T509— Price, per box of 50.....$1.98

50 CIGARS $1.98

Papa

Grandpa

A fine domestic smoke at a very... Made and recommended by one of... cigar manufacturers in the U... made from carefully selected... 4¾ inches long. Shipping...
87T527—Perfecto.
87T525—Londres.

$1.69

Nationally Known Brands

50 CIGARS $2.39
50 CIGARS $1.59
50 CIGARS $1.59
50 CIGARS $2.39
50 CIGARS $1.98
50 CIGARS $1.59
50 CIGARS $1.77
50 CIGARS $2.19

James G. Blaine.
Cut Porto Rican and domestic filler. Connecticut binder and Sumatra wrapper. 4½ in. in length. Perfecto shape. A popular, advertised cigar. Shipping weight, 1½ lbs.
87T613—Price, per box of 50.$2.39

Junius.
Has domestic filler. Connecticut wrapper. 4½ inches in length. Perfecto shape. Shipping weight, 1½ pounds.
87T577
Price, per box of 50.......$1.59

Sunol.
First at the Post. A domestic cigar, about 4⅝ inches in length. Perfecto shape, each cigar banded. A good value at the price. Shipping weight, 1½ pounds.
87T579—Price, per box of 50.$1.59

Lillian Russell.
Made entirely of domestic tobaccos. It is recommended to us by one of the oldest and largest cigar manufacturers in the United States as being a very high grade smoke at the price. About 4¾ inches in length. 50 cigars, banded, to the box. Shpg. wt. 1¾ lbs.
87T617—Price, per box of 50.$2.39

Two Orphans.
Has Connecticut wrapper and domestic filler. Packed 50 in box. A nice size, free smoking cigar. About 4½ inches in length. Perfecto shape. Shpg. wt., 1¼ lbs.
87T598
Price, per box of 50.......$1.98

Spanish Triumph.
Made entirely of domestic tobaccos, which have been well cured and properly aged, giving the cigar a good flavor. About 4½ inches in length. Perfecto shape. Shipping weight, 1½ lbs.
87T596—Price, per box of 50.$1.59

Postmaster.
Connecticut wrapper, composition Porto Rican and short domestic filler. A good smoke for those who want medium **strong** cigars. About 4¾ inches in length. Londres shape. Shpg. wt., 1¼ lbs.
87T600—Price, per box of 50. $1.77

John Law Cigars.
A banded Londres shape cigar, about 4¾ inches long. Medium short cut, domestic tobacco filler. Smokes free and burns evenly. Shipping weight, 1¼ pounds.
87T605—Price, per box of 50. $2.19

Papa said, "That is the best yet," and told me jokingly I ought to write to the Governor and tell him about it.

But I did write the Governor and what was my surprise a few days later to receive a letter from him! Everybody was amazed. Papa was so pleased he took the letter to the store and showed it to everybody who came in. Well, nearly everybody.

"Well young lady," said Grandpa Scott, "What's this I hear about you corresponding with the highest official in our State Government? The next thing we know you will be throwing your hat in the ring."

And he gave me a silver dollar!

"Throwing your hat in the ring" means running for public office.

Original Price Cut in Half

$75 Columbia Princess Grafonola and 6 Records

Grafonola
Alone - $32.10
Records - 3.90
Together, *Our Price* $36.00 *Freight Paid*

A fortunate purchase makes it possible for us to offer you your one best opportunity to purchase a graphophone. By taking the manufacturer's entire stock of this model, we are able to sell the Princess and 6 records for $36.00—less than one-half the ordinary price of the instrument alone. You can't buy a genuine Columbia Grafonola at a cut price anywhere else, and you can't buy the Princess elsewhere at any price.

The Princess is a genuine Columbia Grafonola—a superb instrument. Thousands have been sold at double our price. Now you can get this same instrument, together with six double disc records for $36.00, less than half the original price of the instrument alone. We can make this astonishing offer because we purchased the manufacturer's entire stock of this model—a limited number—and so secured it at a remarkably low price. You can't buy the Princess elsewhere, and when our limited stock is gone you won't be able to buy it **anywhere**. If you don't order quickly you may lose forever this wonderful chance to get a grafonola for **your** home.

With the Grafonola for $36.00 we give six of our "Music-on-Both-Sides" records, to be selected from the list on pages 728 and 729. You may select any of these records, but be sure to give second choice. If you wish to buy the grafonola separately, the price is $32.10.

Remember, there are no delivery charges for you to pay. We deliver the Princess freight paid to your railroad station, no matter where you live.

A Concert in Your Own Home

The Princess will delight every member of your family, your friends, your guests, for it appeals to the love of music that is in everyone. With the Princess in your home you can always enjoy the pleasures of good music, without leaving your easy chair. By your own fireside, surrounded by your family, you can enjoy the best music of the world. Moreover, the Princess will entertain your friends and guests. With a grafonola in your home you can always offer visitors a delightful concert.

The Princess brings you the music as it has been rendered by the most accomplished musicians of the day. The quality of the music produced by other instruments depends upon the skill of the player, while, no matter what your musical ability may be, you are always sure that the music of the Princess will be the best.

All the New Improvements

The mechanism of the Princess is practically the same as that of grafonolas costing double. In the Princess the reproducer—the soul of the instrument—is exactly the same as that on a $200.00 grafonola. The Princess has all the famous Columbia improvements which give it the matchless Columbia tone. The Princess has the new, improved Columbia tone control shutters, sound amplifying chamber insulated from the motor, speed regulating device. It has a double spring, silent, smooth running motor—every known worthwhile device for faithfully reproducing musical sounds. It will play any disc record of any make that is playable with a steel needle.

Aside from its marvelous entertaining qualities, the Princess is also valuable as an addition to your furniture. It is built and finished like a grand piano, elegant in design and of exquisite workmanship. It is made of beautiful figured mahogany in the form of a graceful French table, 31 inches high, with an 18-inch top.

The wonderful qualities of the Princess make it a most profitable investment, one that will pay you returns in pleasure every day. We guarantee that it will please you in every respect—if you are not satisfied your money will be returned at once. Our price includes all delivery charges.

Exquisite French Table Cabinet

13V13 Princess Grafonola Outfit, consisting of the Columbia Princess Grafonola, 6 double disc records to be selected from pages 728 and 729, and 300 needles. Be sure to give catalog number of records desired, and second choice.
Price, complete outfit, freight paid by us....................................**$36.00**

XVI

"Things have changed more," said Father, "in the thirteen years since 1900 than in the 200 years that preceded. Do you realize, Lily, my quarter section in Buchanan County that I paid $7,000 for in 1900 is worth $20,000 today?"

"Good gracious," said Mama.

"That's a rise of $81 an acre, from $43 to $124 in a thirteen-year period."

"Just think of that," said Mama who was trying a new crochet stitch called Lazy Daisy.

Father puffed his cigar, a Flor de Mehlhop, furiously.

"Blow some smoke rings, Papa," I said, so he did. He can blow better rings than anybody except Uncle Ed Scott, Mama's brother, who can blow three rings inside each other.

"Just think," he went on, "you've got a telephone in your house, you can call up your mother and father six miles away any time you like. Inside plumbing! Hot water! Caruso in your parlor on the talking machine! Moving pictures!"

"The portable vacuum cleaner!" said Mama getting into the spirit, "The Majestic Bread Maker! The Fireless Cooker!"

"Roller skates!" I shouted. "Peanut butter!"

"Yes, Lily, it's the greatest age the world has ever seen. And we're right in the middle of it. Julia, by the time you're my age, say 1940, you'll be living in a world of total perfection, total perfection."

"O Papa, 1940!" I said. "That sounds so funny. I don't think there will ever be such a year."

"Peace and prosperity," Papa said. "That's what's ahead, Lily. Art, music, intellect, peace, love — all go with good farm prices. Why, corn is selling at sixty cents a bushel, Lillian."

"My, you are certainly wound up," said Mama. "To what do we owe today's sermon of hope?"

"Miss Otto says Germany is surrounded by people who hate and envy her," I said. "She says there will be a war."

"Nonsense," said Papa. "The German and the British royal families are all intermarried. Why, Queen Victoria was Kaiser Wilhelm's own grandmother!"

This is a practical demonstration of one of the important uses of the Inter-phone system in the home. It means that no matter where the house-wife is she can immediately communicate her wishes and orders to any other part of the house or to the stable or garage. Much time and annoyance are saved by this simple device which means the control of the house from boudoir or drawing-room. A full description of the many advantages of this Inter-phone system will be found in the accompanying article and the page of illustrations showing the different types of Inter-phones will be found useful to those wishing to install such a system.

WESTERN–ELECTRIC INTER–PHONES.

"Goodness gracious what has set you off, George?" said Mama.

"I went out to Scottdale to see your father the Judge today about the Wilcox mortgage," said Papa. "Lillian, do you know what your mother has had installed in the manse? An inside telephone! So she can call from the upstairs sitting room to the kitchen, the laundry, and the stable! What a country! New miracles every day!"

"Blow some more smoke rings, Papa," I said, and he did.

Vehicle Store

A year's use usually brings out the difference between a good vehicle and a poor one. The good rig stands up, runs true and easy, is always ready for use and gives its owner an endless amount of pleasure, pride and service. The other kind of rig seems to lose its real efficiency about as soon as it loses its high finish.

We handle the kind of buggies and wagons that **make good** and **make friends** for us. For example, every spoke in every wheel of every Monarch wagon we sell is bone dry hickory. You won't find a trace of moisture and you won't find any putty filled holes in the wood either.

And the **right kind** of wood is used for every part. Poplar for the sides, ends and seat panels; long leaf yellow pine for the bottom; hickory spokes; oak hubs. Gear woods are all soaked in linseed oil after finishing and before ironing. Rims riveted—heavy irons all around. Just compare construction, material and prices on the style of wagon you want and **see how much our prices save you!**

The same big values apply on buggies. Look at the Empire State Leader—at $54.95. It has all the style any man wants, is built of good, sound material, nicely finished throughout. Any dealer would have to ask $75.00 for a buggy as good.

Look at **all** the illustrations—read **all** the descriptions of vehicles shown on the following pages and you will revise your ideas of what **good vehicles** should cost.

Every Overland vehicle is sold on thirty days' road test, backed by **legal binding five-year guarantee** against defects in material and workmanship. We consider that the only right way to sell vehicles.

XVII

If you think the horse is out of date here in Iowa just because of the invention of the automobile you are all wrong.

Practically all of the farmers depend on the horse to get to town because the roads are so bad when it rains that horses are the only things that can get through. An automobile will sink way down onto the axles and running boards. The mud is three or four or five feet deep. It's a quagmire. It's worse than a hog wallow.

"Well, you can't have everything," says Papa. "It's because of our rich soil. The better the soil, the poorer the roads."

"It's a disgrace," says Mama. "Uncle Herbert wanted to motor over to see us from Milwaukee but said he didn't dare. Why, Iowa is known as the 'Mud Road State' all over the Union."

"Well, anyway," said Papa, "I was spared a two-day filibuster from Uncle Herbert about his hero, that grinning clown Teddy Roosevelt."

"Your Mr. Wilson is a sourball," replied Mama.

The richest man in town is Mr. Victor Squires. He has a large villa set in white pine trees. This villa is of red stone which was brought in here on the Northwestern Railroad all the way from Wisconsin. He has fountains and a dumb-waiter in his house and when he goes to a funeral he wears a silk hat like President Wilson and ex-President Taft at the Inauguration. Everybody calls him "Lord" Squires but not to his face.

He has a big Hudson car with glass windows called a limousine. One day last spring he and Mrs. Squires were out for a ride with their "chiffonier" and they got stuck in the mud out by the Simmons place on the old river road. They had to ride home in an old buckboard wagon right through Main Street.

However, he laughed about it as he is not as stiff as you might think. Anyway the Hudson limousine was stuck out there for three days and they finally had to use three teams, a six-horse hitch, to drag it out of there by main force, as it was nearly out of sight.

There are a few tractors and steam traction engines around in the county but as Papa says, "Nothing will ever take the place of the horse on your Iowa farm. Besides, everybody likes horses."

Saturday afternoon my friend Harriet H. and I went to town. All the farmers and their wives and children were in town and I never saw so many horses and rigs lined up in my life — road wagons, top buggies, runabouts,

No. 2F251 Pipe Cleaners. Just the thing for smokers, as it cleans pipe and stem thoroughly, insuring a clean, cool smoke and making the pipe taste better. A big bargain. Wt., 3 ounces. Price, 24 for...... **2c**

No. 2F347 Full Size First Quality Corn Cob Pipe, with reed stem. Wt., 1 oz. Price.............. **2c**

No. 2F235 One Pair Light Wrought Steel Strap Hinges. Length, open, 6 inches. Wt., 7 oz. Price, per pair...... **2c**

No. 2F233 One Pair 4-Inch Light Wrought Steel T Hinges. Wt., 6 oz. Price, per pair...... **2c**

No. 2F236 Japanned Iron Pull, for barn or heavy doors. Length, about 6 inches. Wt., 8 oz. Price.......... **2c**

No. 2F202 Wrought Hasp with staples. Length, 8 in. Wt., 5 ounces. Price.............. **2c**

No. 2F341 5-Inch Wrought Iron Gate Hook and Staples. Wt., 3 oz. Price.............. **2c**

No. 2F273 Short Handled Stove Shovel. One piece, heavily japanned. Wt., 7 ounces. **2c**

No. 2F203 Cold Handle Stove Lid Lifter. Nickel plated, full size. Wt., 5 oz. Price.............. **2c**

No. 2F370 Handy Iron Holder (asbestos lined). Wt., 2 oz. Price......... **2c**

No. 2F245 Berry or Ice Cream Set. Consists of six papier mache saucers and six paper doilies. Very handy for parties, etc. Weight, 2 ounces. Price, per set......... **2c**

No. 2F305 Waxed Paper Drinking Cups. A very handy and sanitary article for farmers, picnickers, travelers, etc. Each package contains twelve cups folded flat for carrying in pocket. Wt., 3 ounces. Price, per package.... **2c**

No. 2F313 Wire Fly Killer. Wt., 2 oz. Price.............. **2c**

No. 2F369 Handy House Brush. Fiber. Lgth., 5 inches. Wt., 2 oz. Price.............. **2c**

One Furniture Caster, with very hard wood wheel, also called lignum vitae, and grip neck socket. Will stand hard usage. Wt., 3 ounces.
No. 2F242 1-Inch Wheel.
No. 2F243 1¼-Inch Wheel. Price, each.... **2c**

No. 2F286 Tin Double Match Safe. Wt., 3 oz. Price.............. **2c**

No. 2F345 Fancy Pattern Old Copper Finished Metal Drawer Pull. Complete with screws. Length, 3½ inches. Weight, 1 ounce. Price.............. **2c**

No. 2F327 Plain Brass Plated Door or Drawer Pull. Diameter, 1 inch. Weight, 1 ounce. Price.............. **2c**

No. 2F247 One Brass Plated Furniture Handle. Size, 4 in. Wt., 2 oz. Price.... **2c**

No. 2F216 One Dozen Assorted Non-Rustable Nickel Plated Brass Safety Pins. Weight, 1 ounce. Price, per dozen.. **2c**

No. 2F219 Hardwood Toothpicks. About 1,200. Wt., 7 oz. Price...... **2c**

No. 2F220 Receipt Book. Pocket size, about 2x6¼ in. About fifty receipts. Wt., 2 oz. Price....... **2c**

No. 2F362 Set of One-Piece Metal Shirt Buttons. Wt., 1 ounce. Price, per set... **2c**

No. 2F270 One Pair Round Elastic Sleeve Holders. Wt., 1 oz. Price, per pair........ **2c**

No. 2F301 One roll of Fine Toilet Paper. Wt., 5 oz. Price........ **2c**

No. 2F361 Full Coil (about twenty washers) Adjustable Leather Axle Washers. Wt., 1 oz. Price.............. **2c**

No. 2F300 Foot Scraper. Cold rolled steel, japanned. Width, 6 inches. Will not break when used in cold weather. Wt., 7 oz. Price.............. **2c**

No. 2F232 Malleable Iron Picket Rope Swivel. Size of eyes, ⅝ and ¾ inch inside. Wt., 3 ounces. Price.......... **2c**

No. 2F306 Japanese Fan. Length, closed, about 8¾ inches. Wt., 2 oz. Price.............. **2c**

No. 2F250 Children's Bib. Good quality. Wt., 1 ounce. Price.............. **2c**

No. 2F258 Collar or Flange. To fit 6-inch stovepipe. Bronzed finish. Wt., 3 oz. Price.......... **2c**

No. 2F268 Hardwood Butter Ladle. Size, 4x9 inches. Wt., 3 oz. Price.............. **2c**

No. 2F315 Iron End Clevis. Size opening, ⅞ x2⅜ in. Wt., 10 oz. Price.. **2c**

No. 2F272 Heavy Japanned Iron Breast Strap Slide. Width, 1½ inches. Wt., 8 oz. Price.............. **2c**

No. 2F283 Japanese Table Mat. Length, about 7 inches. Protects the table from hot dishes. Weight, 1 ounce. Price, each...... **2c**

No. 2F354 Children's A B C Plate, tin. Diameter, 6 inches. Wt., 2 oz. Price.............. **2c**

No. 2F360 Brass Plated Extension Rod. For sash curtains. Extends 21 to 38 inches. Diameter, ⁹⁄₁₆ in. Weight, 4 oz. Price.. **2c**

No. 2F246 Two Dozen 5-Inch Lace Paper Doilies. An excellent value. Wt., 1 oz. Price.............. **2c**

No. 2F363 Scouring Soap. Cleans pots, pans, glassware, kettles and all kinds of kitchen utensils. Regular 5-cent kind. Wt., 12 oz. Price.... **2c**

No. 2F200 One Bar Laundry Soap. Actual weight, 7 oz. 100 bars to case. Price, per bar........ **2c**

No. 2F285 Tin Nutmeg Grater. Length, 5 in. Wt., 2 oz. Price...... **2c**

No. 2F205 Mouse Traps. Easy to set. A sure killer. Weight, 2 ounces. Price, 2 for.......... **2c**

No. 2F201 Asbestos Stove Mat. Used to prevent food from scorching, to protect table from hot dishes, and as rests for flatirons. Diameter, 8½ inches. Wt., 3 oz. Price........ **2c**

No. 2F349 Hairpin Cabinet. Containing sixty hairpins, assorted lengths, both straight and crimped. Wt., 2 oz. Price...... **2c**

No. 2F358 One Dozen Leather Hair Curlers. Length, 4 inches. Wt., 1 oz. Price, per dozen.... **2c**

No. 2F294 Good Quality Lace Paper Edging for Shelves. Five-yard rolls. Width, about 2½ inches. Weight, 6 ounces. Price, per roll........ **2c**

No. 2F224 One Pair Wrought Steel Shelf Brackets. Size, 3x4 inches. Wt., 4 oz. Price, per pair.... **2c**

No. 2F277 Hatchet Handle. Hickory. Length, 14 inches. Wt., 6 oz. Price.............. **2c**

No. 2F278 Hammer Handle. Hickory. Length, 14 in. Wt., 6 oz. Price.............. **2c**

No. 2F335 Pants Hanger. Keeps pants in shape and prevents wrinkling. Width, 8 inches. Weight, 3 oz. Price.............. **2c**

No. 2F336 Skirt Hanger, same as above, but 12 inches wide. Wt., 5 oz. Price.. **2c**

---

2 Cents ♀ Each

No. 2F209 Wire Coat Hanger. Heavily tinned. Very rigid and will not rust. A very useful article. Width, 17 inches. Wt., 6 oz. Price.... **2c**
No. 2F379 Children's Coat Hanger. Width, 12 inches. Weight, 3 ounces. Price.... **2c**

stanhopes, surreys, farm wagons, brewsters, and I don't know what all. I wouldn't have been surprised to see somebody pull up in a rockaway coupé.

I shopped for Mama and got her (1) a pair of #7 knitting pins; (2) a dozen A.C.E. dress fasteners; (3) six yards of bias seam tape; (4) a bottle of Nervine tonic; (5) two postcards of the Courthouse.

I also got myself a hair ribbon to go with my green velvet corduroy.

I am certainly glad I don't live on a farm.

XVIII

About a month ago Mr. Hammer came one day to give Mama an "estimate" on wallpapering the front bedroom. The boys call him "Beadeye" Hammer because his eyes are rather small and squinty. He is a painter and paper hanger but he calls himself a "decorator" now because he says that's what his brother in Kansas City calls it and he is in the same business over there.

"How much does old Beadeye want for the bedroom job, Lil?" asked Papa when he came home from the store for noon dinner which was ham, hominy and cornbread.

"Six dollars," said Mama cautiously.

"Thunderation," said Papa striking his fist on the dining room table. "Jesse James rides again! An outrage! I won't have it!"

"Well, dear," said Mama, "nice wallpaper is fifteen and twenty cents a double roll nowadays. And it will take Mr. Hammer three hours to hang it."

"Tell him 'No'," said Papa. "I'm not a cripple yet. I'll hang it myself. I don't know what the world is coming to. Six dollars! How about it, Julia, will you and Millie help me?"

"O certainly, Papa," I said, "but do you think we can?"

"Americans can do anything, Julia. Think of the Wright brothers," Papa said.

"Yes and the Smith brothers, too," said Mama, "and their cough drops."

Papa sent for a wallpaper sample book (FREE) which arrived in about a week from Chicago. We had lots of fun looking at the samples which were so pretty, and all disputing in a friendly way over which was to be the chosen pattern. Finally we left it up to Mama and she picked by chance my Second Favorite which was sort of yellowish flowers and speckly dots. Included with the samples was a booklet (FREE) called "How to Hang Your Own Wallpaper."

Exactly nine days later on a Friday, Mr. Pugsley the mailman brought the parcel post packages of wallpaper. They were on the settee in the front hall when I got home from school. Exciting!

"This is going to be a regular vaudeville show," Mama said to Papa over supper which was boiled dinner followed by iggly stewed fruit. "Arnold, let's you and I go down to the Dreamland and see the moving picture."

Brass Beds

Rich in Beauty of Design & Finish

$13⁸⁵

No.5V2230

These Five Remarkable Values

represent the maximum quality at the minimum cost. Their attractive designs, durable construction, beautiful finish and low cost will surprise and delight you. Every home in America can now afford the satisfaction and pride of possessing one or more of these handsome, sanitary brass beds. They are guaranteed to give you perfect satisfaction. **See opposite page for detailed descriptions.**

$19⁹⁵

$17⁹⁰

No.5V363

No.5V361

$8⁹⁵

No.5V2232

See Opposite Page for Full Description of the Five Beds Shown On this Page

No.5V362

$13⁶⁵

"Yay," said my brother and rushed from the table to haul in his hods of coal for the base burner.

Father retired to his Morris chair to study "How to Hang Your Own Wallpaper."

The art of hanging wallpaper requires thoughtful attention. Fortunately Papa is a very methodical person.

In the afternoon Millie and Arnold and I had moved the brass bed and all the furniture to the middle of the room and taken down all the pictures so all was in readiness.

Millie mixed a batch of paste in the kitchen while Father and I set up the sawhorses and long wide boards to cut and paste on.

"The more things you know how to do in life the better," Papa said. "Your husband will get a girl who knows how to hang wallpaper, Julia. And yours too, Millie."

Both of us girls giggled and Millie said, "T'will be a lucky man who leads Miss Julia to the altar, sir," and I said, "Now hush up, you two."

We hung the first strips very carefully to "get the feel of it" as Papa said. Soon Millie and I were cutting and pasting at a great rate and Papa was up on his ladder hanging, brushing it down smooth, rolling the seams and calling for more paper.

When Mama and Arnold got home from the motion pictures we were nearly finished.

"O you wonderful people!" cried Mama. "It's just beautiful."

Father could not help smiling.

"It looks even prettier than the sample," said Mama removing her gloves, "and you saved six dollars."

"It's the principle of the thing," said Papa rather smugly.

Mama brought up cider and some fresh doughnuts Millie had made, while we finished.

"How was the screen play?" I asked my brother Arnold.

"O it was that cheesy Mary Pickford," he said. "They call her Little Mary!"

"Pooh," he added. "The way she bats her eyes is a shame."

XIX

IOWA'S PRIDE, THE DELICIOUS APPLE
Prize Essay by Julia Harrington

"An apple a day keeps the doctor away" says the old adage. Yes, the healthful properties of everyone's favorite fruit are well known the world over. Whether baked, fried, made into sauce or pies, shouts of joy can always be heard when the tasty apple makes its welcome appearance. And what can be more delightful on a cold winter's night than to sit by the fireside while Mother Nature's frigid fingers freeze village, dale and prairie, the whiles biting with eager joy into a crisp succulent homegrown Iowa apple?

"Stay me with flagons, comfort me with apples," says the Good Book, proving that even in far-off Holy Land the founders of the church enjoyed the precious fruit. And in a more humorous vein our own beloved American poet Eugene Field adds:

> "The best of all physicians
> Is apple pie and cheese!"

But most apple fanciers, and who is not, prefer above all to eat the plain pristine fruit as it comes from the tree in order to savor to the full its rare and special flavor. And what variety comes immediately to mind, eclipsing all others, when an "eating apple" is the subject in view?

The Delicious! The Delicious to be sure! What other apple but the famed Delicious casts its mouth-watering spell on all who taste its blushing charms. Pride of America, and glory of the State of Iowa, all hail to the Delicious, the finest apple in the world!

And why is it the glory of Iowa? you say. Because it first blossomed here under our prairie sky, it was born and raised in the Hawkeye State, it is a true and noble Native Iowan. And thereupon hangs a tale of mysterious fate. For it was only by the queerest chance that the King of Appledom came to flourish on earth.

In the last century a man named Jesse Hiatt owned an orchard a few miles northeast of Peru, in Madison County, Iowa. A chance seedling had sprouted up in this orchard. Nobody paid it much mind. And because it was out of line in the row of trees, Mr. Hiatt cut it down in 1870. But the next year, as though by magic, it had grown up again bigger than ever.

"If you must live, you may," said Mr. Hiatt and he let the seedling grow.

Ten years later Mr. Jesse Hiatt entered the house and cried, "Ma, there is bloom on my new apple tree."

Later on, the little tree bore one solitary apple. Mr. Hiatt carefully pared the apple and tasted it and exclaimed loudly, "Ma, this is the best apple in the whole world!" Mr. Hiatt was a Quaker and always called Mrs. Hiatt "Ma." And thereupon he named the apple the "Hawkeye."

For eleven years he tried to raise interest in his pet apple but nobody took notice of the apple orphan's future. He was quite dejected by it all.

But in 1893 Mr. Hiatt sent four specimens to a fruit show in Louisiana, Missouri, which is on the Mississippi River. Mr. C. M. Stark of Stark Brothers Nursery finally discovered the fruit of the chance seedling that had once been cruelly cut down.

Mr. Stark promptly purchased all rights to the tree in Madison County and gave it the new name of "Delicious." Since then it has become the most prized apple in the world, exceeding in popularity even the McIntosh.

And so we add one more triumph to the heritage of Iowa, the finest state in our glorious Union! May the Delicious apple, proud Iowan, flourish forever, bringing joy and health to young and old!

> Essay Contest — The Iowa State
> Horticultural Society,
> May, 1914.

Note: The First Prize was won by a boy from Strawberry Point named, of all things, Bismark Vogenthaler! It was about <u>corn.</u> Second Prize was won by Miss Lillian Botsford of Belle Plaine, the subject <u>also</u> being corn! I won Third Prize. I am very proud of our Iowa corn also, but it is so tedious sometimes. My prize was a Watermans Ideal Number Two 14 Karat Gold Pen overlaid with solid sterling silver beautifully engraved openwork and solid sterling silver safety clip.

J. H.

XX

School is over. I've graduated.

I'll be going to High School next fall and I wish I were not. I did love the old school so. All of us girls had a party for Miss Prohaska and presented her with a 10 Karat solid gold genuine pink cameo brooch. Amy Western got it for us at a "discount" at her father's jewelry store.

The party was very gay but it ended up rather tearfully. Miss Prohaska said we would always be her dear girls and that we must come to see her. Still, it will never be the same again.

O I think growing up is absolutely horrid and Harriet says we will wear corsets in High School and put our hair up. Corsets is one thing but I said to Harriet "I shan't put my hair up, I shan't, shan't, shan't, shan't, shan't, so there!"

Harriet got rather flouncy and went home. After supper I went over and made up and we played "Uncle Josh's Visit to New York" on the Victrola and made divinity fudge with Harriet's little sister Susie.

Harriet's mother came in later from taking some pound cake and jelly to the Widow Brown who is sick. She said we could look at the scrapbook that she kept as a girl. She has it wrapped up in a silk scarf in her bureau drawer.

She explained that in her day thousands of advertising cards were printed for every conceivable product and putting them in a scrapbook was a national craze.

"I had seven large albums full of the most beautiful cards imaginable," she said as she ate a piece of divinity, "but I lost all but this one when the old homestead in Breckinridge County, Kentucky, burned down. I was visiting Alma Louise Purcell in Louisville and I had this one with me."

She comes from Hawesville on the Ohio River and says there is a town down there called "Rabbit Hash." She has a southern way of speaking that is very pleasant.

She said we mustn't worry too much about leaving grammar school and she recited an inspirational poem which was designed to cheer me up.

She is a very nice woman but I think she crowded her picture cards too much. Of course that is because she had so many.

O dear, I suppose everything will turn out all right.

12 X 15
Gingham
$3.75

12 X 18
Linene
$3.19

12 X 16
Repp
$2.89

12 X 17
Gingham
$4.98

12 X 19
Chambray
Gingham
$5.98

10B2094
Crepe de Chine
$2.98

10B209
Plaid Taffe
$3.25

12 X 20
Voile
$3.98

National Cloak and Suit Company. We Guarantee Your Money Back if You Want It

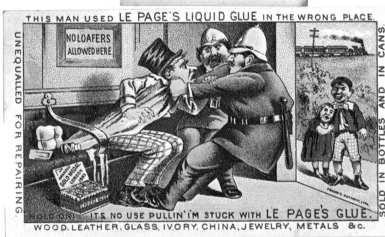

Rootbeer

When the HIRES is passed around

Did you get yours?

XXI

One Sunday Millie Flanagan was sick so when Mama and Arnold and I went off to church Mama put the roast in the oven and told Papa when to take it out.

Mama and Arnold and I go to the Second Presbyterian Church on Dakota Street, the Reverend Percy Osgood. Papa doesn't go to any church because he is a Unitarian and there is no Unitarian Church here in Winnebago. The nearest one is in Cedar Rapids, I believe.

Mama teases Papa.

"Well, George," she says, "I hear they are starting a Unitarian Church here in town. Won't that be lovely for you? You can get all dressed up every Sunday and go to church instead of squirrel hunting with Ben Bonson and Pete Karberg."

"Splendid news," says Papa, "but actually I am a Universalist and a Universalist would not be caught dead in a Unitarian church."

"That's the only way we are ever going to get you into a church," says Mama. "O George, you are a scream."

Anyway this Sunday when Millie was sick we went to church and the Reverend Osgood's sermon was very lengthy as usual. It was about the war in the Balkans, motorcars, President Wilson, and people in Chicago who go to cabarets.

When we got home Papa was sitting on the porch swing reading the Happy Hooligan comic in the **Des Moines Sunday Register and Star** and smoking his meerschaum pipe.

"How does the roast look, dear?" Mama said as we came onto the porch with our white gloves and prayer books.

"Thunderation!" cried Papa. "The roast!"

We all went into the kitchen and smoke was coming out of the oven. Papa took the roast out of the oven with the ice tongs and threw it in the yard.

Not only that but he had been making a batch of Hires root beer and had five gallons all bottled on the kitchen table. As Mama said, the kitchen looked as though Coxey's Army had just marched through.

The Home Delite E-Z bottle capper, the siphon bottle filler and strainer, the funnel and the kettle and extra crown bottle caps were all strewn every which way.

Magnificent Palms in Natural Grandeur

Symmetrical in shape and possessing all the attractive beauty of genuine palms. Will retain their natural appearance for an indefinite time. All the pleasing features of real palms at a fraction of the cost.

The magnificent foliage and stately grandeur of the palm has been the subject of many of the most beautiful and touching southern songs and stories. In short, the palm is a living, breathing part of the sunny south, inseparably connected with its interesting history of love and war. The manufacturer of these palms has attained a degree of excellence equalled by no other maker of this class of goods. The fresh, green beauty and graceful shape of the original palm is copied so closely that one can scarcely realize he is not gazing upon the real article. A number of these palms placed about the room give the exact appearance of a beautiful southern grove, with its silent invitation to rest and luxurious ease.

Made with removable leaves, which permits of cleaning as often as may be necessary. Remove leaves from tin tubes, concealed under bark of tree, wipe with a damp cloth or sponge and replace and the original beauty is restored.

The excellent materials and strong make recommend our palms to those who desire the best. They are not affected by heat or cold, and are as desirable in winter as in summer. Tin tubes are concealed beneath the bark, into which the leaves are inserted, each being numbered and tagged so that anyone can put them in place. This permits packing in a compact form, thus lessening freight charges, and allowing trees to be stored in a small space.

$2.90

No. 16H101P Palm tree, 5 to 6 feet high, 12 removable leaves. Each _____

No. 16H103P Palm tree, 7 to 8 feet high, 12 removable leaves. Each _____ **$3.75**

No. 16H105P Palm tree, 9 to 10 feet high, 18 removable leaves. Each _____ **5.75**

No. 16H107P Palm tree, 10 to 12 feet high, 24 removable leaves. Each _____ **6.85**

Above prices include green wooden tub in which to set tree.

"O George, you have used up all my bottles for ketchup," cried Mama.

"Wait until I put on a clean collar and I will take you ladies to the grand dining room of the Hawkeye Hotel."

He did and we had a beautiful Sunday dinner although there was nobody eating there except some drummers from St. Louis and old Mrs. Peabody.

The Hotel Hawkeye is very grand and has cut-glass decanters, fans going around overhead, and beautiful potted palms in both lobby and dining room.

Papa did something wrong about the root beer because about a week later in the middle of the night the bottles started to blow up, frightening poor Millie who is very nervous anyway and always looking under her bed to see if there is a burglar there, almost to death.

At Sunday dinner at the hotel we had Royal Anne cherries for dessert. I have only had them once in my life before because they are so expensive.

MISS LIBERTY, AT DAWN'S FIRST PEEP
AWAKES THE ECHOES FROM THEIR SLEEP

"I'm Going off on the 4th"

4th July

"Fourth of July" Greetings

XXII

Yesterday was the 4th of July.

The boys get up so early and at dawn you can hear firecrackers exploding all over town. My brother Arnold has been doing odd jobs and saving money and he had <u>four dollars'</u> worth of fireworks. He had cherry bombs, Chinese crackers, cannon crackers, aerial bombs and torpedos.

Finally I got up and had breakfast and called up Harriet on the telephone to come over. Harriet's number is 311. Our number is 89. Grandpa Scott's number is 3 because he had the third telephone in town.

Harriet came over and we crunched our red spit-devils on the sidewalk. They can't hurt anyone if you are careful. Then we sat on the porch steps and lit our snakes. You have to be careful not to inhale the snake smoke.

Then Harriet ran home to get dressed for the parade. I had on my white marquisette with red, white and blue sash and hair ribbons to match. Harriet had the same according to our plan. Both our families walked to the parade together.

The parade was a great success and we were very proud when the "Hawk eye Juvenile Band" marched past led by Drum Major Floyd Krantz the barber. My brother Arnold made us thrill with pride as he gallantly strutted past in his blue and gold uniform, making the most tremendous notes with his big silver B-flat tenor slide trombone. Fatty Clark was beating out paradiddles and flamadiddles and I don't know what all on his snare side drum and I must say he looked handsome. I nudged Harriet and said "There's Fatty Clark," and she said "Yes, he's a fine drummer isn't he?"

Mayor Lucius P. Lord gave a speech from the bandstand in the park that Papa said was pushing everybody's patience away too far. A switch engine was shunting cars in the railroad yard beside Garfield Park and making a terrible puffing and clanging. It would go away and then when it would come back the Mayor would talk louder and louder until he was shouting.

Uncle Roy and Aunt Ellen drove over from Falls City in their new seven-passenger Peerless touring car. Uncle Roy owns a line of grain elevators and is very well-to-do.

Papa and Uncle Roy had some cherry bounce while we ladies, including

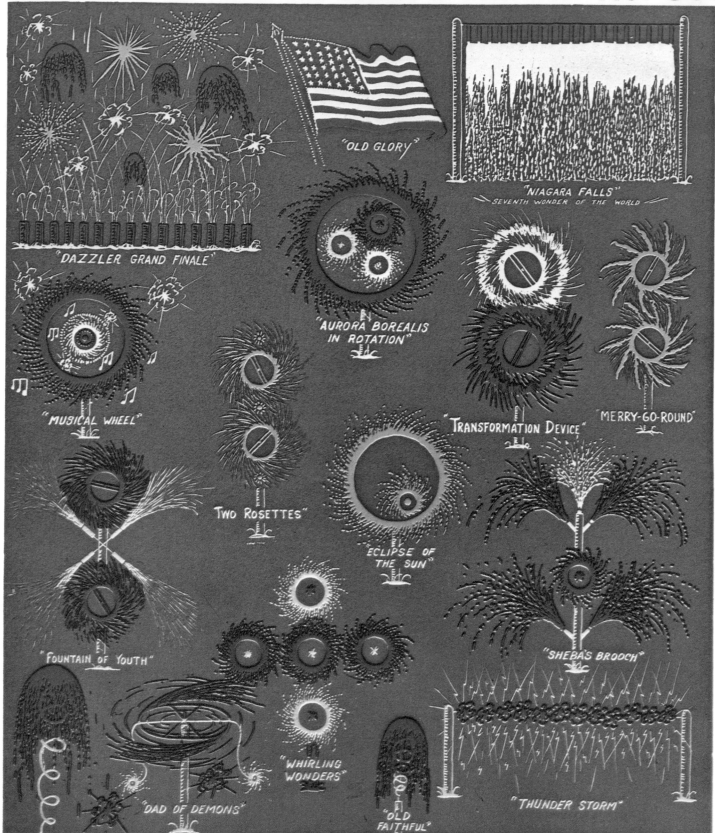

"DAZZLER GRAND FINALE"

"OLD GLORY"

"NIAGARA FALLS"
SEVENTH WONDER OF THE WORLD

"AURORA BOREALIS IN ROTATION"

"MUSICAL WHEEL"

"TWO ROSETTES"

"TRANSFORMATION DEVICE"

"MERRY-GO-ROUND"

"ECLIPSE OF THE SUN"

"FOUNTAIN OF YOUTH"

"SHEBA'S BROOCH"

"WHIRLING WONDERS"

"DAD OF DEMONS"

"OLD FAITHFUL"

"THUNDER STORM"

"LEGION EMBLEM"

LIST OF SET PIECES AND DEVICES

Musical Wheel	Pyrotechnical Girandola
Two Rosettes	Fountain of Youth
Dad of Demons	Sheba's Brooch
Whirling Wonders	Thunderstorm
Eclipse of the Sun	Old Faithful
Aurora Borealis In Rotation	Niagara Falls
American Legion Emblem	Old Glory
Merry-Go-Round	Dazzler Grand Finale
Transformation Device	12 Red Torches

my two little cousins Mae and Josie, sat on the side porch and had lemonade and fresh Independence Day flag cookies sent to town from Grandma Scott.

Then Papa and Uncle Roy decided to shoot off Grandpa Harrington's flintlock musket. Mother and Aunt Ellen protested vehemently but to no avail. Little Mae and Josie began to cry and such a hubbub!

First they couldn't find the gunpowder and then the flint was loose. Arnold was sent to the barn to look for the gunpowder over the workbench. We ladies all went into the house and I took little Mae and Josie upstairs to see my doll-house and they stopped crying.

Presently there was a terribly loud boom outside and after a few minutes another one. This gun has been in our family since the Revolution. Papa and Uncle Roy came in quite disheveled and smudgy and had some more cherry bounce.

Tonight was the Fireworks Display out at the Fair Grounds and beautiful it was. I have never seen such glorious set pieces, to see them and think patriotic thoughts sends tingles up one's back.

As we were leaving and standing under a street light my cousin Harry Fielding came up and said hello. He lives on the far side of town on the way to Scottdale. "Are you going to the High School this fall, too?" he asked Harriet and she said she was.

"I am President of the Glee Club," he said, "and I hope you will join."

"I don't know whether I sing well enough for that," Harriet said blushingly.

"O fudge," I said. "You know Harry, she sings in the Episcopal choir."

"Bully," said Harry. "Then I'll see you at High School. And maybe before that if Julia will ask me over some time."

We walked home slowly. The whole town seemed to smell of smoke and gunpowder.

"He is on the football team as well," I said.

It is over 90 degrees tonight and not a breath of air stirring. The crickets and the seven-year locusts are giving a deafening concert all their own.

The Easiest Way to Can Your Fruit
Put it Up Now to Cut Next Winter's Food Bills

Peaches   Green Gages   Strawberries   Pears   Currants   Blackberries   Quinces   Cherries   Apricots   Pineapple

All These Fruits May be Canned in One Way and Without Sugar

FRUITS may be divided generally into "soft" and "hard" groups. In the soft group we have apricots, blackberries, blueberries, cherries, currants, dewberries, figs, gooseberries, grapes, huckleberries, peaches, plums, raspberries and strawberries. After hulling, seeding, stemming or skinning the fruit, place it in a strainer and rinse by pouring cold water over it. Pack into clean hot jars without crushing, using a big spoon or ladle.

All fruits can be successfully canned by the cold-pack method without the use of sugar by simply adding hot water. In canning fruit with sugar the sirup should be prepared in a separate vessel and poured over the fresh fruit in the hot jar.

In preparing the hard fruits, like apples, pears and quinces, remove the skins and cores, cut into convenient slices and drop into slightly salted cold water to keep from tarnishing. Pack closely in hot jars.

To can either soft or hard fruits, either with or without sugar, process—that is, keep under the vigorously boiling water—for the length of time given in the sterilizing table on Page 22, which is the time for quart jars. If you live more than 1000 feet above sea level the time should be increased one-tenth for every 500 feet over 1000. Upon removing the jars, tighten the covers, invert to cool and test for leaks. Wrap in paper, and store.

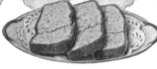

Home-Canned Peaches With Potato-Flour Sponge Cake for Dessert Next Winter

Quince   Pineapple   Apricots   Strawberries

Strawberry Preserves on Boiled Rice Will Save Sugar Next Winter

Peaches   Plums   Cherries

Blackberry   Currant   Grape

Gooseberry

Raspberry

Apricot

White Cherry   Peach

Quince   Apple   Crab Apple

Jellies With Cream Cheese and Rye Crackers at Luncheon Next Winter

Damson Plum

Quince

Serve Pineapple Jam With Corn Muffins on Cold Mornings Next Winter

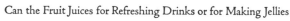

When Jelly is Done

THERE need be no uncertainty about making jelly of good quality if this simple test is made: After the fruit has been boiled and the texture broken down it should be poured into a jelly bag and permitted to drain. Twelve ounces of sugar added to a pint of juice will make a jelly of the proper firmness and texture. Jelly is ready to be poured into the glasses when, upon testing it, two rows of drops form on the edge of a spoon held sidewise.

Can the Fruit Juices for Refreshing Drinks or for Making Jellies

HOT fruit juice may be poured into ordinary jars or hot bottles and handled like the canning of the fruit itself. If poured into miscellaneous bottles make a cotton stopper, press into the neck of the bottle and leave during the sterilization period. Set the bottles in boiling hot water up to the necks. Sterilize the fruit juice for forty minutes at a temperature of 165 degrees Fahrenheit. Remove, and immediately press corks in over the cotton stoppers. If the cork fits well no paraffin need be used. If a poor cork it may be necessary to dip the cork in hot paraffin. Fruit juices handled in this way will keep fresh. They may be made into jelly when the new apples come, or whenever it is convenient to buy sugar.

NOTE—Attention is called to time and sirup table on Page 22.

To Make Sure it Will "Jell"

PLACE two teaspoonfuls of the unboiled and unsweetened juice and two teaspoonfuls of grain or denatured alcohol in a glass and mix well. Settle for half an hour. If a jellylike substance forms at the bottom, pectin—the starch-like substance found in many fruits, which is necessary to make the juice "jell"—is present. If not present it may be obtained by combining apples or green citron melon with the fruit, or by adding the white portion of orange peel to the juice.

XXIII

Some of us girls have a Canning Club and a lot of us have our own gardens too. I have twenty-five Atlantic Prize tomato plants (red) and fifteen Volunteer tomatoes (yellow). I have ten Bull Nose green peppers, ten Cherry Red peppers, two rows of Golden Beauty corn and a row of New Fireball Forcing Radishes. I also have several vines of Johnson's Christmas watermelons, the same of Jersey Extra Early Prolific Pickle cucumbers and a dozen horseradish which are grown from sets. Everything else is grown from seed. Packages of seed cost 5 cents and 10 cents. Horseradish sets are 20 cents a dozen.

Of course Mama has a kitchen garden of her own which Papa says is totally unnecessary since her father the Judge has one of the biggest vegetable gardens in the state. But Mama just loves her kitchen garden as well as her "old-fashioned" flower garden. My brother Arnold is on Papa's side for the reason that he has to help Mama weed, cultivate, and spray her gardens on Saturday mornings. He is not at all fond of gardening and I would not dare to ask him for help with mine. I thoroughly enjoy working in my garden. Probably because it is mine. I have found that makes a great difference in life.

Tom Sawyer got his boy chums to whitewash a fence, but so far Arnold has not discovered any way to get Fatty Clark, Earl Huckins, or any of his friends to do his garden chores for him or even help him. They have enough of that at home, I guess.

The last three days our Canning Club has been meeting out at Grandma Scott's farm, Scottdale, to make various pickles. You can't make pickles in one day. We all go out in three cars: one Ford, one Overland, and Mr. Clark's Sears-Roebuck. The Sears-Roebuck only holds three people and is built like a buggy and is very uncomfortable but fortunately I rode in Bessie Van Tapscott's new 1913 Overland.

The County Agent, Miss Lindstrom, was in charge, assisted by Grandma Scott's cook, Mrs. Kleinschmidt. (What a dreadful name to have to spell all your life!)

We all wear white aprons and white caps and although canning is hard work if you look at it that way, we all have a fine lark as well as "the warm glow that comes from achievement" as Miss Lindstrom says. Miss Lindstrom

71

ATLANTIC PRIZE.

New Fireball Forcing Radish.

The shape of this exceedingly valuable new variety is well shown in the accompanying illustration, although it grows nearly twice the size. It is the finest red forcing turnip variety ever introduced; has a very small short top, color brilliant scarlet, crisp, solid, tender, and of fine flavor. It is alike valuable for out-door planting early in the spring or in the autumn, and will always command ready sale at good prices throughout the year. It will not disappoint a single customer who sows it, whether he be a market or family gardener. Pkt., 10c.; oz., 15c.; ¼ lb., 40c.; lb., $1.25.

FOR
FAST TRAIN

CONNECTIONS

JOHNSON'S CHRISTMAS WATERMELON.

Our extensive experience in the growth of all varieties of watermelons for seed in past years, together with the assurance of hundreds of melon growers who have tested it, enables us to assert that *Johnson's Christmas Melon* will, when fully introduced, supersede nearly all other melons for shipping and keeping purposes. Since the original melon was discovered, in 1883, we have each year enjoyed one of these melons for both a Christmas and New Year's dinner, when, after being kept in our cellar for a period of three months, they cut open as fresh and delicious as the day they were picked. Their valuable keeping and shipping qualities are due to a peculiar, hard tenacious coating or outside enameling of the skin, which also gives them an exceedingly handsome and fresh appearance, even after being kept or allowed to remain on the vines for months after ripening. Notwithstanding the rind is quite thin, we have dropped them from a height of four feet without breaking or bruising. The flesh is of a beautiful rich scarlet, *very solid and of delicious, sugary flavor.* Its uniform size and handsome, fresh appearance, at all times, make it a *most salable variety.* Pkt., 10c.; oz., 20c.; ¼ lb., 40c.; lb., $1.25; 5 lbs., $5.00.

is from North Dakota and is Swedish and talks with an accent. She is very pretty and Papa said the other day, "If I was twenty years younger Miss Lindstrom would not be County Agent very long and her name would miraculously be changed to one beginning with the letter H."

However Mrs. Kleinschmidt did not seem to be entranced with Miss Lindstrom's overpowering beauty and in fact got quite grumpy and disapproving over some of Miss Lindstrom's instructions and canning methods.

"She's as stubborn as Maud's goat," Papa always says. "It comes from a lifelong diet of sauerkraut."

I have never discovered who Maud is or why she had a particularly stubborn goat. One time when I was "looking peaked" Dr. Bigelow recommended goat's milk. It was a horrible experience.

We can right out in the open at Grandma Scott's on tables set up on the lawn under the maple trees. On the third day we finished our pickles. Here is what we put up:

Banded Dixie Relish
B. S. Chutney
Sweet Pickled Chayote
Mixed Dixie Relish
Vegetable Macedoine

B. S. Chutney is packed in red and yellow bands in the jars. These colors represent the banner of Spain and for this reason it is called Banner Spain or B. S. Chutney. We canned from 9 A.M. to 6 P.M. with 45 minutes off for a lunch of cold chicken, fresh bread, and soda pop, a surprise from Grandma Scott. We certainly were tired as we wended our way homeward through the "fields of waving corn."

Papa is crazy about pickled chayote and ate about a third of a jar with his supper, which was beefsteaks, green beans, summer squash, home-fried potatoes, Perfection Salad, and Parker House rolls. They are named for a hotel in Boston, metropolis of the Bay State.

Emily Gardiner came by and asked me to walk downtown with her to buy her mother the new **Delineator** but I was too tired from canning. You just can't sit down while canning.

I have personally 63 jars of pickles.

Next week for tomatoes.

C.H. PECK, DEL.

C FAUSEL, LITH.

AMANITA CAESAREA Scop

ORANGE AMANITA.

XXIV

It was Sunday and Papa hired a rig at the Livery Stable and Papa, Arnold and I went out to Butternut Hollow by the Antelope River to gather mushrooms. Mama said it was much too dreadfully hot, she would sit in the porch swing with a good palm-leaf fan while we "adventurers" sallied forth.

Mama was right. It was _hot_; the big Selz Royal Blue Shoe thermometer on the telephone pole by the Livery Stable said 99 degrees. I have seen it 111 and Papa says he has seen it 114 in Manitoba. Papa has been most every place in North America.

I am not very much use on a mushroom expedition as I hate to even touch them. Arnold is not much better. Papa knows all about where to look for them and which are which and we soon had half a market basket full.

The German Saengerbund had set up tables under the trees by the river and were having a Beer Picnic. They had a keg, steins, heaps of sauerkraut and ribs and hot potato salad and all such things. Papa was invited to join them for a stein of beer and Mrs. Stettenmaier took me under her wing so to speak, and saying "I know what girls like," she sat me down and put a piece of _custard pie_ in front of me. Well! If there is anything I fondly _dislike_ it is custard pie, especially when the water or whey has separated and it is all sodgy and the crust is also sodgy. I can't bear it!

Well, what could I do? I managed to get one bite into my mouth and gagged terribly and thought I might expire right on the spot. The second bite was even worse. I knew I could never finish. Just then Mrs. Stettenmaier got up to go get herself another stein of Dubuque "Star" beer at the keg.

Quick as a flash I slipped the whole piece of gooey custard pie in my apron pocket!

But my trial was not over yet. When she came back, seeing I had "finished" my pie she immediately forced another piece on me saying "Mine gootness, I nefer zeen nobody ate pie zo vast in mine life." However this time I politely refused and ran off (with an apron pocket full of _custard_) to join Arnold, some of the young people, and some of the ladies, too, who were swimming in the river.

Papa laughed heartily all the way to town about the incident of the custard pie in my pocket.

When we got home Millie was about to cook beefsteaks for supper and

Women's, Misses' and Children's Bathing Apparel

Cap 39R83 69¢

39R3145 $2.98

Cap 39R67 39¢

39R3093 $2.25

39R3007 98¢

39R3059 1.49

Cap 39R51 23¢

Cap 39R75 49¢

Cap 39R59 35¢

39R3073 98¢

39R3137 $1.98

39R3047 $1.19

Shoes 7R1689 25¢

39R3051 1.49

Shoes 7R1690 25¢

39R3007 Child's One-Piece Bathing Suit of fine elastic ribbed wool mixture, reinforced seams and double gusset at crotch. Sizes, 2, 4, 6 and 8 years. State age.
39R3007 Navy blue trimmed with white.
39R3009 Red trimmed with white. **98c**
Our price..............................

39R2995 Child's Cotton Ribbed One-Piece bathing suit. Reinforced seams and double gusset at crotch. (Not illustrated.) Sizes, 2, 4, 6 and 8 years. State age.
39R2995 Navy trimmed with white.
39R2997 Red trimmed with white. **49c**
Our price..............................

39R3093 Women's and Misses' Elastic Ribbed bathing suit of fine wool mixture. Waist, skirt and tights made in one piece. Tights have elastic cuffs at knees. Reinforced seams and double gusset at crotch. Sizes, 28 to 44 inches bust measure. State size.
39R3093 Black. 39R3095 Navy. **$2.25**
Our price..............................

39R67 Women's and Misses' Swimming Cap of mottled or rainbow rubber. Boudoir style, with rosettes and streamers of contrasting color. Elastic band adjusts cap to fit any head.
39R67 Mottled trimmed with Red.
39R69 Mottled trimmed with Navy. **39c**
Our price..............................

39R3145 Women's Smart Bathing Slip-on suit, made of wool mixed mohair. Stylish princess model with wide sailor collar, wing sleeves and loose belt. Collar, sleeves and belt trimmed with white braid. Sizes, 34 to 44 bust measure. State size.
39R3145 Black, White Trimming.
39R3147 Navy Blue, White Trimming. Our price..............................**$2.98**
See 39R3073 for Undergarment.

39R83 Women's and Misses' Rubber Turban for swimming or bathing. Trimmed with striped rubber ribbon in butterfly effect.
39R83 Red.
39R85 Green. **69c**
Our price..............................

39R3047 Women's Fine Cotton Jersey "California" bathing suit, consisting of complete undergarment with skirt attached. Shield sleeves held in place by tape tied over the arms. Tights have elastic cuffs at the knees and double gusset at crotch. A wide white double sash makes an effective finish. Sizes, 34 to 44 bust measure. State size.
39R3047 Black.
39R3049 Navy. **$1.19**
Our price..............................

7R1689 Women's and Misses' Black Duck tango bathing shoes. Duck cork soles lined inside with white muslin. Laces with each pair. Sizes, 1 to 8. State size. Our price, pair.. **25c**

39R3059 Misses' Combination Bathing Suit of whipcord cotton serge. Waist and skirt in one piece; separate bloomers. Square neck, short sleeves. Bloomers have elastic at knee and draw string at waist. Sizes, 28 to 32 bust measure. State size.
39R3059 Black and White.
39R3061 Navy and White. **$1.49**
Our price..............................

39R51 Women's and Misses' Rubber Tam O' Shanter bathing or swimming cap, trimmed with beautiful rainbow rubber in contrasting color.
39R51 Red. 39R53 Navy. **23c**
Our price..............................

39R3137 Women's Bathing Slip-On or Suit of wool mixed mohair. V neck, wing sleeves and shoulder closing. Neck, sleeves, belt and bottom of skirt trimmed with white braid. Sizes, 34 to 44 bust measure.
39R3137 Black trimmed with white.
39R3139 Navy trimmed with white. **$1.98**
Our price..............................
See 39R3073 for undergarment.

39R75 Women's and Misses' Popular Model bathing turban of live rubber. Trimmed at sides with pretty rosettes of white rubber.
39R75 Navy Blue. 39R77 Green. **49c**
Our price..............................

39R3073 Women's and Misses' Worsted Plaited one-piece bathing suit. Low neck, sleeveless model. Ribbed cuffs at knees. Double gusset at crotch. Sizes, 28 to 44. State size.
39R3073 Black. 39R3075 Navy. **98c**
Our price..............................

39R3069 Women's and Misses' One-Piece bathing suit (not illustrated), of fine cotton Jersey cloth. Low neck, sleeveless style. Double elastic ribbed cuffs at the knees, and double gusset at crotch. Sizes, 28 to 44 bust measure. State size.
39R3069 Black. 39R3071 Navy. **49c**
Our price..............................

39R59 Women's and Misses' Rubber Swimming or diving cap. Trimmed with fancy rubber ribbon butterfly bow in front.
39R59 Red.
39R61 Black. **35c**
Our price..............................

39R3051 Women's Two-Piece Bathing Suit of whipcord cotton serge. Combination waist and skirt; separate bloomers. Square neck, short sleeves. Trimmed with facings of striped Galatea. Bloomers have elastic at knees and draw string at waist. Sizes, 34 to 44 bust measure. State size.
39R3051 Black, White and Black Trimming.
39R3053 Navy Blue, White and Navy Trimming. Our price.. **$1.49**

7R1690 Women's and Misses' Black Duck tango bathing shoes. Good-wearing duck cork soles lined on the inside with white muslin. Laces with each pair of shoes. Sizes, 1 to 8. State size. Our price..............................**25c**

Papa said he would like the mushrooms to "go mit." Neither Mama nor Millie would have anything to do with the project so Papa got out

COMMON SENSE
IN THE HOUSEHOLD
a manual of
Practical Housewifery
by
Marion Harland
New York
Charles Scribner's Sons
743 and 745 Broadway
1871

This is Mama's favorite cookbook and she says it may be old-fashioned but she was "raised on Marion Harland."

The first thing that struck his eye was the following sentence which he read aloud from page 244:

"Not being anxious of martyrdom, even in the cause of gastronomical enterprise, especially if the instrument is to be a contemptible, rank-smelling fungus, I never eat or cook mushrooms."

"Dear Miss Harland seems to have swallowed the dictionary," Papa ejaculated contemptuously. "She must be from Boston."

Papa then cast **Common Sense in the Household** to the winds, rattled up the stove and opened the drafts, after which he prepared his mushrooms and put them in a porcelain pot with water and proceeded to cook them. Millie kept talking about people who had died horrible deaths from eating mushrooms. She was looking pale and flustery.

After they had been cooking about fifteen minutes Papa said:

"Why, what's this, Millie? The spoon has turned black!"

"Holy Mother of God! Sure 'tis the pizen coming out of them devils. Don't eat 'em, don't eat 'em!" Millie cried and fainted dead away onto the linoleum floor.

Millie was sprinkled with water and revived, I helped her to her room to lie down, Mama cooked dinner, and Papa ate his mushrooms.

It was the hottest day of the year in Iowa: 109 degrees, the hottest since 1911 when it was 111 degrees, and 1901 when it was 113 degrees.

What with record heat, mushrooms, Millie fainting and custard pies in pockets it was a rather memorable day in the life of

Yours Most Sincerely,

J. Harrington

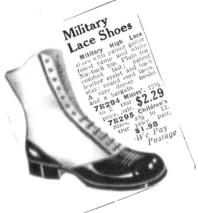

XXV

Papa took me to <u>Dubuque</u> and back on a business trip. This is a long trip. I rode on <u>four</u> trains. The purpose of the trip was to visit the crockery and glassware jobbers to place orders for Papa's store, the EMPORIUM, and do other business.

Papa wanted to give us a treat and ride to Clinton on the "Overland Limited," which is an elegant fast express from San Francisco to Chicago. Since it doesn't stop here in Winnebago we went to Marshalltown on the local train. Mr. Holmes the conductor said he hoped I would not break too many hearts in Dubuque. He is so silly. I had on my Norfolk-style shepherd check coat with Copenhagen blue trim.

We had only a short wait in Marshalltown when the Limited came roaring in like a monster and soon we were in our "section" in the Pullman which Boomer Leach the agent at home had secured for us. I had never been on a Pullman before and it is so different from an old smoky day coach! As we sat in the dining car eating lovely things we thundered through Winnebago. It was a strange experience indeed to see Sullivan's Livery Stable, the Hawkeye Hotel, and familiar Main Street go whizzing past like a flash.

I would like to eat <u>all</u> my meals every day for the entire rest of my life in a dining car on a railroad train rushing through countryside, village and town. Nothing can compare.

After our superb repast we repaired to the "Buffet, Smoking and Library Car," which was grand beyond imagining. You won't believe it but there was a Barber Shop as part of this car.

"My entire ambition in life since I was a penniless orphan in the docks of Liverpool," said Papa, "has been to have my hair cut on a speeding de luxe express train."

And he did, while I sat in a velvet chair with tassels on it reading free magazines and having soda pop that had come all the way from California, and Vienna sugar wafers by Van Derveer and Holmes of New York.

Papa was not an orphan and has never been in Liverpool.

Here are the stations between Marshalltown and Clinton:

Marshalltown
Quarry
Winnebago
Le Grand
Montour
Tama
Long Point
Chelsea
Belle Plaine
Luzerne
Blairstown
Watkins
Norway
Fairfax
Cedar Rapids
Bertram
Mount Vernon
Lisbon
Mechanicsville
Stanwood
Clarence
Lowden
Wheatland
Calamus
Grand Mound
De Witt
Malone
Low Moor
Camanche
Clinton

We reached Clinton at 5:33 and O how I regretted to get off that beautiful train.

"I am sorry my dear that we cannot ride on the bosom of the Mississippi to Dubuque," said Papa as we waited for our train connection. "But the fine old Diamond Jo Line is gone blooey, bent, busted and bankrupt. I never thought I would live to see dark days when you couldn't ride a fine packet from St. Louis to St. Paul."

"Never mind, Papa," I said. "There will always be grand express trains with velvet cushions and barber shops and palace dining cars."

"They've made the Steamer <u>Sidney</u> into an <u>excursion boat</u>!" he cried, and lit a Spanish Triumph cigar and puffed on it madly while he regaled me with tales of packet days and Captain Diamond Jo Reynolds whom he had met in 1897 in person.

We boarded the Chicago, Milwaukee and St. Paul and after passing through Lyons, Sabula, Savanna, Green Island, Bellevue, Gordons Ferry and Massey we were in the metropolis of Dubuque. It was a pleasant ride with views of the Mississippi River but a day coach is not a Pullman and old Train Number 6 on the Milwaukee is not the Overland Limited streaking for Chicago.

We stayed at the Julien House. I sent postcards to all at home.

The Julien House is named for Julien Dubuque, a French Canadian who opened lead mines here and was the first settler.

The next day Papa took me with him while he conducted his purchases at C. H. Little, Bruce and Company — Wholesale Crockery, Glassware, Lamp Goods and Fancy Goods. Mr. Bruce gave me a doll's tea set for a present. I hadn't the heart to tell him that I don't much play with dolls any more. O well, I shall give it to my chum Harriet's little sister Susie.

For a surprise Papa and I picked out a new dinner set for Mama. It was called Princess Louise and has sprays of white roses, autumn leaves and green moss fern. The 56-piece set cost $3.62 wholesale.

The rest of the day is a jumble in my memory it was so filled with startling impressions.

1. A ride to the top of the bluff in a cable car called the Fenelon Place Elevator.

2. An open-air streetcar ride. I have been to Des Moines but never in an open-air trolley.

3. Levi's Dept. Store where Papa bought me a pair of Military High Lace shoes with patent gaiter foxed vamp and white Nu-buck top with patent leather eyelets and back stay. Delicious!

4. The H. B. Glover Company where Papa placed orders for drop shipments of men's winter underwear, as well as harvest jackets, husker mittens, wool caps, overalls, notions, and outing flannel nightshirts. Mr. Parker was nice to me and gave me a sample card of buttons and a back comb with eight imitation emeralds right out of stock.

5. Boldt's Confectionery! Impossible to describe!

6. Papa ate <u>oysters</u> at the Wales Hotel with me, Mr. and Mrs. Nicholas Duttenhoefer, and their son Frederick. Mr. Duttenhoefer is the Brewmaster at the Dubuque Malting Company, the biggest brewery in Iowa. He is an old friend of Papa's from New Vienna when they were boys. Frederick is fifteen

years old and plays the Boehm system clarinet and has been to Milwaukee three times. If anybody asked me if he was handsome I would have to say "Yes."

7. ! ! ! ! ! ! ! ! Miss Maude Adams in "Peter Pan" at the Grand Opera House! ! ! ! ! ! ! ! ! ! ! ! ! ! ! ! ! O I have never laughed and cried so much in my life. Frederick sat next to me and bought me a box of "opera creams."

I'll never forget that night as long as I live. The whole two days were like a trip to Fairyland.

It all seemed so strange when I got back to Winnebago. I tried to tell Mama about everything in Dubuque but failed miserably. "I understand, dear," she said.

Three days later I got a letter from Frederick. Yes, I told him I would write if he would write first.

"Mrs. Frederick Duttenhoefer!"

Wouldn't you just know it?

XXVI

September 20, 1914.

High School starts tomorrow.

We all went to the Church Supper tonight and walked home together afterwards. We've had a dry summer and leaves are beginning to fall.

Everything was quite still as we walked down Osage Street except for the puffing of Number 34, the "yard goat," or switch engine, down by the depot. Iowa seemed to be all around us.

I said goodbye to Harriet at her gate and Arnold and I walked home behind Mama and Papa. I think I will always remember the smell of Papa's cigar (a Flor de Mi Gusto) this night as we strolled home down the old familiar street.

Everybody talks about the wicked war in Europe. Grandpa says the "Four Horsemen" are riding again and this time they will ride on and on.

Papa says the war will be over by Christmas.

My piano lessons have become a "shambles" as Mama would say. Miss Otto plays "Deutschland, Deutschland Über Alles" and sticks pins in a map of Europe.

I did an odd thing tonight. I got all my old dolls out of the wicker hamper that they live in under my window and made them comfortable in the big easy chair in my bedroom.

I don't think I will write any more about life in Winnebago.

I hope things turn out all right.

Love,

Julia

No, I am not <u>sad.</u> I got a letter from Frederick today. He is enrolled at the Devereux Military Academy, in Montezuma, Iowa, and asked if he could come to us for Thanksgiving!

Ethel, our cow with the silly name, has gone dry! Thank Thee O Lord for small favors.

GOOD BYE

JULIA HARRINGTON

SEPTEMBER
1914